MAVERICK
AMONG THE MOGULS

Life is Short
The Art Long
Occasion Instant
Experiment Perilous
Decision Difficult

From the Library of
BENSON B. ROE

MAVERICK AMONG THE MOGULS

The Adventurous Career of
A Pioneer Cardiac Surgeon

An Autobiography
by
Benson B. Roe, M.D.

CREATIVE ARTS BOOK COMPANY
Berkeley • California

For information contact:
Creative Arts Book Company
833 Bancroft Way
Berkeley, California 94710
1-800-848-7789
Fax: 1-510-848-4844
www.creativeartsbooks.com

ISBN 0-88739-424-8
Library of Congress Catalog Number 2002102141

Printed in the United States of America

To my wife, Jane,
who provided unflagging support
and sound wisdom for this scenario
while sharing a good part of its
vicissitudes, frustrations, uncertainties,
and even its glories.

Acknowledgments

I am indebted to my critical and supportive friends for their detailed critiques of the manuscript in successive drafts; first, to Owen Jameson whose vast legal experience and English scholarship provided valuable perspective and detailed suggestions; second to Dr. Francis Moore, my most illustrious and scholarly mentor, whose review pointed me in the right direction, third to my son David, whose literary talent made his critique extremely beneficial, and finally to Paul Samuelson in our publisher's office, whose meticulous editing is responsible for the final product.

Table of Contents

Foreword

It has been my impression that autobiographies worth reading were ego trips reserved for impressive, important, or at least interesting people, none of which I ever considered myself to be. However, with the leisurely perspective of eight decades and the urging of my good friend Lillian Ross of *The New Yorker* I finally recognized that my life *has indeed* been an interesting, unusual and, in some ways, astonishing story. This conviction arises not from the modest accomplishments that I can claim but rather from a series of unlikely events, which were my fate, and which evoked an attitude and behavior on my part that would not have been predicted. Hopefully the following pages will convey an image of an amusing paradox.

Writing has always been a pleasure for me, though I have produced little worthy of note in a bibliography of 177 papers, chapters, editorials, and one textbook. It can, however be said that both my career and many of those writings have been controversial. Whatever, success they may represent could have been improved with a better non-scientific education and a better ability to compromise between integrity and diplomacy.

Sadly inconsistent with my standard advice to aspiring medical students, my own undergraduate curriculum was too sparsely marked with the humanities and English and too heavily consumed with the scientific courses in the pre-med program. Nor did I have the benefit of a prep school discipline that so many of my medical colleagues had enjoyed. The origin of my bent for writing remains obscure but if there were to be any such thing as reverse genetics I could attribute my meager expressive capabilities to my children, one of whom is a skilled writer and both of whom are exceptionally articulate on their feet.

As to how I developed an urge to tilt against windmills while preserving a pretty solid image of conventional trappings is equally mysterious. That I did, however, has been the source of much pleasure and satisfaction on the one hand while also daunting to my political progress on the other. Survival to a comfortable state of (pseudo-) retirement must be credited to a lot of good fortune but also to those mentors and institutions that were sufficiently flexible and tolerant not to reject me summarily for rocking the boat. That appreciation also goes for my parents and certainly for my wife of fifty-six years, who played an important role in much of my behavior—undoubtedly sparing me from a far worse fate.

*I have come to the conclusion that my
subjective account of my own motivation
is largely mythical on almost all occasions.
I don't know why I do things.*

J.B.S. HALDANE

MAVERICK
AMONG THE MOGULS

CHAPTER 1

Who Said "Maverick"?

O n July 3, 1981, the *New England Journal of Medicine* published an editorial I had written, titled: "The U.C.R. Boondoggle—A Death Knell for Private Practice?"[i] This relatively casual contribution of constructive intent turned out to be the crown jewel in my unintended but growing reputation as a maverick. Some have labeled it "traitorous" and worse. How it came about is of interest in the context of a career that has defied logic and probability, a crazy series of events that are inconsistent with a properly behaved, conservative, unsophisticated, middle-class Depression-bred boy from the West, which many then considered to be culturally deprived.

The article recites the explosive and abusive pattern of charges by physicians and other health care providers in a system of remuneration that I considered to be so fundamentally flawed as to invite those abuses. My knowledge of that process derived from a role I had acquired casually as a solicited consultant to Blue Shield of California to adjudicate the validity of selected, seemingly unusual fees submitted by cardiothoracic surgeons. I was appalled by what those reviews revealed. Charges were escalating at an alarming rate along with the introduction of imaginative billing techniques that had no rational justification, and that were minimally curtailed by the third-party payers. This pattern of steep inflation— by all health care providers—had no predictable end point and threatened to bankrupt the nation. As I saw it, the only ones capable of stemming the flood were physicians themselves who controlled not only their own charges but who were responsible for authorizing nearly all the other charges. My thrust was to expose the atrocity of irresponsible billing in the hope of persuading the profession to address the issue before massive

bureaucratic control became a necessity. (The concept of corporate own-
ership of medical practices had not yet emerged but that sad eventuality
was certainly fed by the system I was deploring.) Most physicians are
inherently honest people and have traditionally been compassionate about
the financial limitations of their patients. In the days before insurance and
Medicare, when personal pocketbooks were the sole source of revenue,
doctors were either unable or—in many instances—unwilling to collect
their fees from a significant portion of their patients. But the introduction
of third party payers in the impersonal roles of government or huge corporate entities changed the behavior of physicians and/or their office managers. Gradually, it became a challenge to find ways of getting more money
from these amorphous entities. Physicians exaggerated or duplicated or
even fabricated the services they claimed to have rendered. Traditionally,
technical procedures had been "packaged" (one fee for preparation, all
aspects of the operation and postoperative care) but that custom was
replaced by multiple entries, sometimes broken down into ridiculous triv-
ia. For example, it is always routine to leave a temporary drainage tube in
the chest after a heart or lung operation and was always considered to be
part of the procedure, but some surgeons began to bill separately for doing
so. When a procedure was more difficult or complex than usual surgeons
added to their routine charge but never reduced the charge when it was
easier or simpler than usual. Practices like these—by both physicians and
hospitals—contributed significantly to a dramatic escalation of health care
costs. A deeply rooted tradition of prodigality in medical care added to the
fundamental waste and inefficiency of standard clinical practice.
Physicians ordered tests and treatments freely with no consideration of
how remote the benefits and expectations might be because there was no
incentive to exercise restraint as long as the cost for them fell on neither
the doctor nor the patient. Although most physicians were aware of these
abuses, which were inherent in the system, they felt helpless to address the
problem as individuals and as long as everyone else was lining his pockets they might as well join the bandwagon. This may sound cavalier but
remember that the profession has never had a well disciplined political
force to keep its own ranks in line, and realistically there was no chance
that the apparent ills would be corrected from within. Thus sensible—
even if not completely honorable—physicians grabbed what they could
take out of the open cookie jar knowing that the lid would eventually be

slammed shut. Subsequent events have borne out the prediction, to the detriment of both physicians and society, and, of course, to the consummate frustration of those who pleaded for reform leadership.

Interestingly after submitting the article I did *not* receive the customary post card from the *Journal* acknowledging my submission and reciting the review process. Instead I received a surprising telephone call from the editor, Dr. Arnold Relman, who indicated that he wanted to publish my article but needed a couple of questions answered. First, he wanted assurance that the dollar figures I had submitted could be documented, which I quickly confirmed. When I inquired about the second question, he hesitated, then asked, "Are you prepared to be tarred and feathered?" I laughed and reassured him that I had no political vulnerability and was prepared to take the consequences. Then put the whole matter out of my mind as an unimportant incident in a busy clinical life.

I was not alerted to the publication date and did not regularly see the Journal so the appearance of the article was unbeknownst to me until the phone rang during dinner at home on July 3. Without salutation, a familiar voice simply exclaimed, "God damn you, Roe!" It was Gil Campbell, one of my outstanding and enterprising surgical colleagues, who called to offer his endorsement and to say that he wished he had written it. In the ensuing weeks I received 155 letters from a broad spectrum of readers—medical students, internists, surgeons, deans, and administrators—nearly all of whom were supportive and complimented my courage to write it. Surprisingly, there was only one vitriolic letter and a couple with partial disagreements. Unheard from were the legions of greedy providers who had become wealthy off the system and were certainly not happy with a whistle blower. Two subsequent editorials in the *N.E.J.M.* extended the theme. The first, titled: "A Challenge to the Health Insurance Industry,"[ii] attempted to place the responsibility and capability on the third-party payers who had the power—if not the incentive—to curtail these abusive practices on the (theoretical but unacknowledged) assumption that their primary responsibility was to the premium-paying public and not to the recipient providers. Since they held the purse strings they could easily have imposed reasonable restrictions on to whom and how much was paid. The second, titled: "Rational Remuneration," proposed a method for determining appropriate charges for technical and professional services in what was essentially a non-competitive system. These elicited much less response from the readership and equally absent response from either the profession or the third party payers. But the issue was on the table.

These editorials resulted in my being called to testify in Washington at Congressman Henry Waxman's Subcommittee on Health Care, at which I made some extravagant statements about the abuses, which resulted in my becoming a pariah in the medical establishment.

What is significant, in light of the dramatic changes in medical practice that have occurred in the middle 1990s, is that *not one* of the numerous professional organizations capable of addressing the issue even made any official recognition of the problem, let alone attempted to correct it. The fact was that so many physicians—and particularly surgeons—were getting very wealthy through the system and were unwilling to upset the apple cart for the mere moral satisfaction of protecting society and a future generation of physicians who would suffer from the consequences of their abuse. They all seemed to know that the bubble would eventually burst but rationalized that there was little they could do as individuals so they might as well grab the booty while it was there to be taken. Now, of course, those few who can remember twenty years back are dubbing me a prophet for what should have been obvious. Predictably, the steep escalation of health care costs had ample airing in the press and became a political nemesis as sacrosanct Medicare was threatened with bankruptcy. Organized medicine attempted to account for those costs on the basis of inherently sophisticated and expensive technology and an aging population that required more care. These factors, of course, did play some part in the process but their role was merely a cover for the much larger cost of widespread overbilling. A prolific redundancy of facilities and physicians in a system that was inherently non competitive did not have the ordinary effect of lowering charges but instead caused prices to rise in order to keep the underutilized physicians and facilities at least solvent and usually affluent.

Another factor contributing to expensive health care was a prodigal attitude ingrained into medical training. We were taught to spare no measure with the slightest chance of medical benefit on the premise that it would be negligent to do so. Because the cost of tests and treatments never came out of the physician's pocket, and because there were no price considerations in the non-competitive process, incentives to control expenses were absent. Providers were basically paid whatever they wanted to charge. It hardly took a financial wizard to foresee a disaster in the making as the inflationary spiral became a cyclone.

In perspective, the period was one of widespread affluence. Professional athletes were commanding enormous salaries, business executives, best selling writers and entertainers were into seven and eight figure incomes, so it is understandable that physicians would righteously justify decent reward for their arduous responsibilities. Of course, they forgot the economic reality that doctor's services did not generate large advertising or profit revenues but instead were only paid for from expense moneys.

The day of reckoning arrived as a result of inevitable pressures from government and industry straining under an enormous and rapidly growing economic burden for health care. When Hillary Clinton's health care reform efforts failed to deliver a politically acceptable solution to the problem, it opened the door for enterprising entrepreneurs to provide a deceptive partial remedy with industrial methods. They recognized how easy it was to trim the huge layer of fat in the system, which was thick enough to provide *both* significant economies to purchasers of health care *and* a rich benefit to the corporate provider. By introducing "managed care", consisting of a few obvious efficiencies to trim prices, the practice of medicine was converted from a laissez-faire, open-ended, unrestricted process to a tightly controlled business. Physicians were the big losers because they were in oversupply and not organized to protect their interests; when pushed to the wall their services could be bought cheaply. In one sweep, they were demoted from masters to drones.

Had their leadership recognized the inevitable and grasped the initiative for sensible reform and economic responsibility there would have been less need for intervention and far less incentive for commercialization. This failure is a tragedy both for the profession as well as the public. The image and posture of a formerly noble profession has been smeared.

Whatever provoked me into taking a righteous stand on an issue that was of little importance to me at my stage of life is perplexing but consistent with my character. Gregarious instincts and craving for peer approval typically dissuades incurring disfavor without strong motivation. I did indeed have a deep affection for my chosen profession and a strong moral sense of its integrity being eroded by greed, provoked by an irresponsible remuneration system. Some were alleged to have said that I was jealous of the wealth my colleagues were accumulating but I was genuinely disturbed by a ballooning process. Maybe it was arrogance that accounted for my action but I did have a strong conviction that disaster was inevitable and that somebody had to say so.

Perhaps the following overview of my life and background will provide an explanation for this behavior and why my surgical mentor, Dr. Edward D. Churchill, labeled me a maverick.

CHAPTER 2

Who Am I?

With the perspective of a long life I can ponder over what labels to wear. At various times and with a wide range of proficiency I can claim identity as author, cardiac surgeon, carpenter, civic leader, expert witness, hunter, lecturer, oarsman, professional leader, reform advocate, researcher, scholar, squash player, tennis player, teacher, university professor, and yachtsman. All of these labels just happened in the course of my life, none without effort, most with some serious intent, but only a few with significant accomplishment.

By all of my own childhood perceptions and from any thoughts conveyed by my family I was just an ordinary, middle-class, conventional, reasonably well-behaved, conscientious, and moderately bright boy who struggled through the rigors of adolescence along with my high school peers in the socially protected setting of the conservative university town of Palo Alto, California. Having skipped a school year in early childhood, I became socially and physically disadvantaged as the result of being younger than my classmates and of being the victim of somewhat delayed puberty. Normal adolescent insecurity was thus compounded, and my behavior was warped accordingly. I was small of stature and pudgy on entering high school but grew some eight inches in two years, to the confusion of my peers, my parents, and myself. Those circumstances were certainly not conducive to anything but a conventional behavior—indeed they were intimidating to an insecure adolescent.

It remains an endless debate over what part of us is a product of his/her genetic makeup and what part derives from experience, environment or individual will. The pattern of our lives is determined by some mixture of inherent characteristic, socioeconomic environment, and fate.

What portion of that pattern is deliberately alterable is a matter of speculation. Certainly fate plays an important role—as I will relate—but statistical reality suggests that luck is less unbalanced than it may appear. Some conjecture that failure derives from neglecting opportunities and/or wallowing in adversity, whereas success is attributed to learning the art of parlaying whatever good luck comes your way and shrugging off the bad luck in stride. Perhaps that ability is inherited, but in any case it is the theme of my life.

My great grandparents were presumably enterprising and courageous—at least for venturing to California in its primitive cultural state before and during the gold rush of 1849. Cesar Bertheau, my mother's paternal grandfather, came by sailing ship around Cape Horn to San Francisco from Hamburg in 1848. Rudolph Jordan, my mother's maternal grandfather, came to Mexico, crossed the isthmus at Vera Cruz, came up the west coast and caught a ship from Mazatlan to San Francisco, also in 1848. Jared Rice, my paternal grandmother's parents, came across the country by wagon from Connecticut to settle in Virginia City, Nevada, where my father's mother was born. Each of these pioneering ventures can perhaps be identified as "maverick" because whatever incentives drove these people from their European origins had to have been coupled with a spirit of nonconformity.

I was born on July 7, 1918, at the Good Samaritan Hospital in Los Angeles, where my father was managing the Linde Air Products Plant during World War I. As the first child of two native San Franciscans and the grandchild of three San Franciscans, the locale of L.A. was an embarrassment that haunted my life because of the intense rivalry between long established "sophisticated" and conservative San Francisco and flamboyant, mushrooming upstart Los Angeles. Before long the family began a series of moves around California that followed my father's motley career; we subsequently lived in San Mateo, Pasadena, Atherton, and Palo Alto interspersed with five different addresses in San Francisco.

My genetic heritage included reasonably solid middle-class grandparents, three of whom were born in the West. On my father's side, George H. Roe came from Ireland. He married Laura Rice whose family, of English origin came to San Francisco. Both my mother's parents, Cesar Bertheau and Anita Jordan, were born in San Francisco. I remain curious about the explanation for why the Bertheaus and the Jordans had abandoned their supposedly solid middle-class European roots to undertake what certainly must have been a major disruption for a quest into the unknown social and economic wilderness that was California. Both of those families were descendants of Huguenots from the Loire valley in France who had fled in the seventeenth century from the Catholic tyranny that followed Louis XIV's rescinding the Edict of Nantes that protected Protestants. They moved first to Amsterdam and then to Hamburg. Europe was in an economic depression overrun with revolution in 1848, but the real motivation for such dramatic relocation was never mentioned in our household. And why they decided to come all the way West instead of stopping in the settled eastern part of the U.S. is equally curious. Whether all of them wandered away from the herd just for the sake of adventure or rather because they caught the fever of California's gold discovery remains unexplained; but wander they did. Perhaps my behavior can be attributed to inheriting that break away impulse.

It is significant that I am an eldest child, that I grew up during the Great Depression, and that my upper middle-class family of modest means was socially pretentious. Both my parents were children or grandchildren of enterprising and successful pioneers of western development. Rudolph Jordan developed a winery in the Napa Valley, called Lotus Farm. George Roe, my father's father, launched the world's first electric utility company in San Francisco, The California Electric Light Company[iii]. My step-grandfather, William Benson Storey, was president of the Santa Fe Railroad and was instrumental in leading to its post World War I success. He allegedly had the foresight to persuade the company's board of directors to abandon the posture of contention adopted by the other railroads that had been conscripted during the war and to accept the government's meager settlement offer and get on with rebuilding. Other relatives fit into that mold: Dick Bertheau, my mother's younger brother, was vice president of New York's Marine Midland Bank and later president of Peoples Trust of New Jersey, Both positions resulted from striking out of the comfortable security of familiar surroundings. None of these relatives was an intellectual giant or a creative genius but this heritage of achievement and adventure was a pervasive stimulus that probably influenced me beyond my basic inclinations and perhaps provoked an instinct to go for the long shots. But I was not consciously influenced by these elements.

Uncertainty shrouds some elements of this family history. We do not know what caused the premature death of George H. Roe at the age of forty-two. It was said to be "Bright's Disease" (kidney failure) but we have no records. My father's only younger sister, Rita, was carefully closeted from the family all her life for reasons that were mysterious because she seemed perfectly normal on the rare occasions that I saw her. We wonder whether she was an epileptic or a psychopath since those problems were the cause of social embarrassment in those days.

It is indicative of our culture that my mother's mother, Anita Jordan, was born in San Francisco and sent back to the family in Hamburg at the age of three, to be properly reared and educated. She returned to San Francisco at eighteen to be presented to society and henceforth to be married to Cesar Bertheau. The German background was pervasive in the family's friendships and travels. This fact was punctuated on an occasion in my grandmother's sixties when she was introduced to someone and replied—without a hint of an accent— "Your face comes to me familiar for but your name does not fall me right away in", which is a literal translation of a German expression.

My father's mother was born Laura Brambilla Rice in Virginia City during its heyday of silver mining in the Comstock Lode. We were told that her father had a feed store and her mother ran a boarding house but, of course, some of us mischievously speculated over whether this was a bawdy house. In Laura's youth, the family moved to San Francisco where she met and married George H. Roe, a young financial broker who had emigrated from Montreal. To the best of my knowledge, his parents had emigrated to Canada from Dublin, where an uncle, for whom he was presumably named, owned a large distillery that produced Geo. H. Roe Irish Whisky. He must have done well because he became the benefactor that financed the reconstruction of the Protestant cathedral in Dublin. My father was always proud of his Irish heritage, which he displayed in his cheer and humor, but I have been reluctant to share that pride because of the senseless Irish determination to slaughter each other over which Christian Church you belonged to.

Both my parents, but particularly my mother, placed considerable importance on propriety and appearance, some of which I rebelled against as I grew up. My mother put more stock in social position than I cared for and I had trouble with her feeling that our family background deserved some kind of distinction or advantage other than what we had earned or achieved. She was a determined woman who manipulated her children's lives into conformity with her objectives and social imagery. Father, on the other hand, was less pushy and gracefully combined an almost royal dignity with an unpretentious manner. His egalitarian humility and Irish humor gave him a charm that made him enviably popular at both ends of the social scale. His affable manner beguiled the hostesses and the grand dames as well as the parking attendant. I loved and admired him for this great skill which I never acquired, yet I resented his failure to make his talents productive.

Our life style during my childhood was quite comfortable by a common standard but our modest middle-class trappings were no match for the social world that my mother coveted. I had, therefore, mixed feelings about being thrust into the company of her wealthy and prominent friends' children. Certainly some pleasure was derived from these associations and a number of my own lifetime friendships derived from them. Nevertheless, I remember the discomfort of feeling poor and embarrassed by comparisons of affluence. This reaction relates indirectly to the aforementioned resentment that my father was a personable, bright, resourceful, and capable person with tremendous opportunity, who ought to "be somebody"—but wasn't. I often wondered what kept him from his apparent potential and was aware that he was reputed to have frail health, though the only evidence of it was a family diet devoid of spicy foods. There was occasional reference to his ulcer which had apparently been well controlled with a surgical bypass. His behavior was either provoked or exacerbated by a domineering mother, who doled out some financial support, and by a wife who was supportive but strong-minded and manipulative. Undoubtedly this perception of him also contributed to my compulsion for achievement and my desire to identify independently. Although I retained all of the conventional relationships, I "left home" spiritually at the age of fourteen with a feeling at odds with the directions and ambitions that my parents, particularly my mother, had for me. This may have been the first manifestation of non-conformity.

Interestingly, my father never made us aware of what must have been a strong resentment that his upbringing in an aura of affluence had abruptly changed in the middle of his senior year at college. What had once been a substantial "Roe fortune" in the stock of a thriving and burgeoning public utility was insidiously dissipated by the negligence of the friend and banker who was trustee of George Roe's estate. Without any prior suggestion that her presumably comfortable financial position had undergone erosion, Laura Roe continued to maintain her somewhat elegant life style in her large house on fashionable Shady Lane in Ross. Then one day out of the blue, her banker informed her that he had been quietly liquidating capital during the sixteen years after George Roe's death in 1894 and that now it was all gone. This dramatic revelation of riches to rags resulted in aborting my father's final year at college before graduation. Exact dimensions of that fortune in today's dollars is incalculable, but G.H.R. is alleged to have held a controlling interest in the California Electric Light Company, which later merged with the San Francisco Gas Company to become the Pacific Gas & Electric Co., later to become the world's largest privately owned utility. I have no knowledge of what share of the merged company he would have owned but it certainly was substantial and if kept in tact it would represent a sizable block of PG&E stock. That the banker was never held responsible for negligent management of the estate is a surprising product of an era when accountability was lax and esteemed bankers were above criticism.

As a money lender George Roe accepted an early electric dynamo as collateral for a loan. Since electricity was in its primitive stage the machinery must have been little more than a curiosity. However, when the debtor defaulted, George, in total ignorance, decided to tinker with it and see if he could make it work, unwittingly risking his life by putting the electrodes in his mouth. Fortunately for him the dynamo was not functioning properly. After it was rebuilt and proven to produce electricity, George started his little company and began selling power for some electric arc street lights in downtown San Francisco, two years before the famous Edison electric plant was built in New York. It then grew rapidly as electric power became widely accepted and Edison's incandescent lamp became available to provide a new modality for both domestic and commercial lighting.

Needless to say, I have fantasized over the possible consequences of being a scion of such wealth; but I also realize that those surroundings would probably have altered my outlook and attitude, with the likelihood of dissipating much of the drive that I acquired in dealing with adversity. Lurking behind my facade of diligence and purpose lies the soul of a suppressed Sybarite who could very easily have become a social playboy. In any case, it is certain that I would have turned out differently under the cloak of affluence that I never knew. To what extent that sequence of events influenced my father's career is impossible to tell, but he never dwelled on it and we never knew what we missed.

Information is lacking about how Laura made out with no money but presumably there were some other modest resources and the large house in Ross must have fetched a good price. Obviously she was socially active enough to meet and be courted by the president of the Santa Fe Railroad, William Benson Story, for whom I was later named. Shortly after their marriage in 1915 they moved to Chicago where they lived in a lovely Lake Shore Drive apartment. "Prexy", as we grandchildren called him, was a handsome, dignified, taciturn gentleman, modestly aware of his power and importance in the railroad world but who had been a "strictly business", socially naive bachelor engineer before yielding to the tutelage of his glamorous new wife. A few years later, they bought a house near Santa Barbara in Montecito where she spent summers and where he came for his sedate month vacation, during which I don't remember ever seeing him without a stiff collar and jacket. Quite a dignified couple they were.

Chapter 3

Growing Up

O ur family life in the quiet college town of Palo Alto was stable, conservative, and generally happy. It focused much more attention on the children than we appreciated at the time. My younger brother George was always a charmer and could get away with murder by laughing and frivolity, which he used adroitly to compensate for what was then not recognized as dyslexia and stammering. My sister Eleanor was quiet and innocently subjected to the will of our domineering mother. Neither of them were part of my social life, except at home where I have vivid memories of regular family games of dominoes, cards and chess, particularly with my father. He built us a tall scaffold in the back yard for various gymnastics. He built a tool shop for us next to his where we puttered in various projects and learned the rudiments of carpentry, plumbing, electricity, and sheet metal work. Though our training in these skills was only rudimentary it turned out to be of great value in my future—not only as a useful handyman around the house but also in the mechanics of developing heart surgery where gadgetry was an almost daily challenge.

My father also gave us our first rifles and patiently trained us how to handle guns safely and to shoot accurately. We had regular sessions out in the marsh where he had target practice with rifles and trap shooting with shotguns. But most importantly he encouraged us to think for ourselves. Dinner table discussions were lively, illuminating, controversial, and open-minded. I can remember nothing of dogma or authoritarianism. That experience contributed significantly to my curiosity and catholic interests as well as encouraging an open-minded approach to every aspect of our lives. My family's conventional background and behavior were hardly the setting for rebellious conduct, but they certainly provided a stimulating forum which required little conformity beyond respectable behavior and discipline was never harsh or punitive.

My father's crowning gesture of free thinking occurred at the breakfast table on the Sunday morning that was scheduled for my confirmation in the Episcopal Church. I was prepared to go through with it having rehearsed in the liturgy and dressed immaculately for the occasion. But I casually mentioned being a little uncomfortable about having to recite a series of "I believes" which I was quite sure that I did not really believe; whereupon my father summarily canceled my appearance at church. He held to this decision despite an emotional complaint from my mother, who was all gussied up for the occasion. I have always appreciated and admired my father for that gesture of simple integrity. It had no serious emotional consequences, except to my mother's parental image, because religion never played a significant role in our family conduct. Indeed dogma was always challenged. But I think that my mother identified the church as part of her social trappings. In fairness, however, it should be reported that we were never overtly inculcated with agnostic ideas and indeed we were sent to Sunday School and services in a variety of churches without pressure toward any particular one or even any pressure to be religious. In a sense, we lived in a paradox of conventional behavior and solid Republican politics insidiously imbued with liberal attitudes. We were thus overtly positioned in the herd but subtly allowed access to an open door.

Although we were never close to affluent, the hospitality of a few friends and relatives provided a glimpse of life's luxuries at various estates in Hillsborough, mansions in San Francisco, a duck club in Los Banos, a ranch in Nevada and yachts on the Bay. The most elegant experience was unappreciated in my youthfulness, at nine or ten, when my step-grandfather took me in his presidential private car on an inspection trip over several hundred miles of Santa Fe track. It was just an engine and his car with a chef and two stewards. We sat on the observation platform where he would spot something of concern, like a trestle, reach up and pull the cord to stop the train and have it back up to let him off to inspect whatever it was. Little boys always love trains but to have a real one of my own (sort of) was a great thrill, particularly when the engineer let me ride in the cab for a while.

The geographical meandering of my family and the tides of their fortune resulted in my attending six separate elementary schools, each of which provided a different flavor and exposed me to some memorable teachers. We lived in San Francisco during my very early childhood. I attended Grant School (in San Francisco's Pacific Heights) for first and second grade, which required my traveling from Russian Hill on the old "Toonerville" double cable car. The following year I was sent to a small private school on Russian Hill, behind the Livermore mansion, run by a Miss Paul who punctuated our studies with a session of playing chess every day. It was a valuable stimulus. The rest of my youth was spent in Palo Alto through its outstanding public school system. In the fifth grade I memorized the 48 States and their capitols, which I somehow retained for life, to the profit of a few wagers. A lust for reading began early and even became the cause of discipline when I was caught reading an Edgar Rice Burroughs novel on the seat between my legs during History class in the sixth grade.

During this period, I was a timid shrimp who kept his distance from the tough guys and just followed the tide without distinction. My academic performance was consistently in the fringe below the conspicuous leaders, always good but seldom outstanding. As noted previously, my normal adolescent insecurity was compounded by a delayed puberty and the social disadvantages of being a year younger than my peers. There must have been a significant psychological impact from a physical metamorphosis when I started high school as a chubby little boy who was shorter than nearly all of my classmates and grew some eight inches to a tall, thin, scrawny bean pole, in two years. This surge kept me from being well coordinated and I was a prime victim of adolescent insecurity. Not surprisingly, I was not noticeably popular or "head of the class" or "athletic hero" but I did manage through diligence to attain modest distinction as a scholar, an athlete and a participant in extracurricular activities. I was an unspectacular member of the swimming and water polo teams, acted in Thespian Club plays, served on the Student Council, and managed the school bookstore. Academics were never difficult but any inspiration to excel was subordinated to a craving for peer recognition and social acceptance.

Those turbulent years in the middle of the Great Depression contained numerous experiences that influenced our lives, though our community was comfortably middle-class and had little ethnic diversity. Coeducational schools afforded exposure to a variety of girls with whom we had frequent social and physical contact. However post-Victorian mores remained in force to shackle our boiling hormones and few if any of us had sexual experience beyond a little innocent necking before graduating from high school. There was smoking behind the barn but I do not recall any drinking, except for an occasional beer, and certainly there were no drugs of any kind.

One indelible episode occurred at a wedding of a good family friend's daughter when I was sixteen years old. This first exposure to champagne resulted in my making a fool of myself in the presence of my parents and their friends. I was taken home by a benevolent colleague and was asleep when my parents returned. The next morning, I dreaded a confrontation over this disgrace, but the suspense was met with silence, presumably because my younger siblings were present. Weeks went by with not a word about the transgression. A month or two later, my parents were off on a trip to New York, leaving me in charge of the house and the automobile. I delivered them to the railroad station, kissed my mother goodbye as she ascended the Pullman car steps, and shook hands with my father. He started up the steps but hesitated and turned back to put his left foot on the little yellow Pullman stool and said, "Oh, by the way, if you do any drinking I expect you to behave like a gentleman, *and don't drive that car.*" This quiet but firm admonition had such an impact that it became a creed which guided my social behavior ever since.

The adolescent drive to achieve recognition in some athletic endeavor was compelling. Lacking the size and stature to play football or the height and speed for basketball I reverted to the water, where I have always felt comfortable. However, my competitive efforts at swimming and water polo were pretty dismal. In a swimming meet I was on the relay team that was leading the race when I dove in for the last lap but lost for my team as result of my miserable performance. Although this participation qualified me for a letter, I was such a disgrace that they booed at the ceremony when it was awarded. Any expectation of athletic prowess was thus laid to rest. At least I thought so at the time. Nevertheless it was, in retrospect, a stimulating atmosphere in which to grow up. Palo Alto High School was populated by many of Stanford's families and provided a quality of education that approached many of the best private prep schools. In that particular school it was virtually taken for granted that everyone would go to college. The proximity and pervasivness of Stanford drew a major segment of my class and, of course, I was attracted to join my friends who were going there. Circumstances, however, pointed me across the bay to Berkeley, thus closing an era of protected, comfortable, and provincial suburban living during the forgettable years of early adolescence. It was not a phase in which there was any inclination to non-conformity. Indeed, the embarrassing social miseries of that period I prefer to forget.

CHAPTER 4

College

There was never the slightest question in our household that formal education might end with high school, nor was there any consideration of going east to an Ivy League college. The only issue was whether it would be Stanford or the University of California at Berkeley (UC), either of which were easily attainable academically. Choice of the latter was the result of tradition, geography, and economics. My father, my namesake step-grandfather, William Benson Storey, and my uncle Dick Bertheau were all UC graduates and strong advocates. The quality of the school was certainly not in question, with a national ranking that rivaled the Ivy League schools. The venue was a factor in response to a strong lure to have this experience some distance from surveillance by my family in Palo Alto. But the hard reality was that Stanford was too expensive.

The Berkeley campus of UC was impressive. Its neoclassic architecture, its tree-lined hillside setting, its vista of the Golden Gate, its illustrious faculty and its large, diverse, by 1935 California standards, student body all contributed to an indelible impression of quality that remains through numerous opportunities for comparison. This experience allowed us to emerge from being yokels into the big world where lots of doors would be opened simply by its affiliation. Although it is nominally a public university without ethnic prejudice, the student body in those days was predominantly upper middle-class Caucasian, similar to that of Stanford and the Ivy League schools.

When I got to college I began to understand the mechanics of peer pressure and subtle competition in the pecking order. My upbringing in the Puritan Ethic provoked a strong urge to do "the right thing." I signed up for the conventional courses, joined the Psi Upsilon fraternity, in

21

which both my father and my uncle had lived, and tried to do what I thought was expected of me in this first adventure away from home. Being part of a great university in a magnificent setting and being taught by stimulating professors was an exciting experience that we did not fully appreciate in our zeal to be accepted and to blossom in the strange new world of maturity. It is a wonder that any of us assimilated significant learning in the midst of so many social distractions. My fraternity must be credited for its policies of requiring all underclassmen to study in their rooms for three hours every week night and its serious concern about anyone's probationary or failing grades. This role of surrogate parent is an unpublicized virtue of the commendable fraternities that taught respect, responsible behavior, and communal participation, along with their better known image of drinking, playing and carousing. This developmental phase of my life was significantly influenced by the fraternity and its thirty-odd members with whom I lived, worked, and played for four years. This group must be credited with my behavioral indoctrination. The first realization of my being off course came at the end of my freshman year, during which I had assumed that my actions had been proper and appropriately subservient. The upperclassmen of the fraternity held a weekly disciplinary session for errant lowerclassmen, particularly freshmen, who had either violated behavioral rules or failed to execute their assigned chores or received an unsatisfactory academic grade. The discipline consisted of being loudly summoned to their gathering, fiercely admonished by the president, and then having your head stuck in a pillowcase while your butt was whacked a prescribed number of times with thin wooden paddles that we had earlier been commanded to fashion from orange crates. While all of my fellow underlings had been paddled at least a time or two for specific infringements, I had managed to escape that fate by manifesting just enough diligence to avoid notice. It was, therefore a rude shock to be called on the carpet and simply told that I was "too cocky," which was deemed sufficiently heinous to be worthy of ten painful whacks. The important but unheralded role of the fraternity system is to bring adolescents through the transition from parental guidance and approbation to the real world of peer acceptance. The realization that I had failed to create the right "vibes" despite a conscientious performance was a rude awakening and the first indication that I was an unintentional non-conformist. It proved to be the bellwether for a career that would subsequently be filled with controversy and paradox.

College life revolved around the fraternity, much as home had been before. Everyone had his own academic, social, and campus activity, but each of those was influenced by fraternity rules, ideas, and attitudes. Freshmen were demeaned, disciplined, and required to study; sophomores were tolerated and provided with a little respect; but not until becoming an upperclassman were we fully accepted. Getting drunk was a regular weekend ritual but there was never any drinking on school nights and the involvement was almost always in the house. There was a strong tradition against rowdyism and conspicuous behavior, called "arm-waving," which was backed up with stern punishment. Though memories of those weekly sessions are fuzzy they seemed to be the acme of conviviality and intellectual rapport at the time. What damage it did to our livers remains to be determined at autopsy, but despite alcohol's reputation for mischief, the Psi U scenario was strong on bonding and it did undoubtedly keep us out of trouble because these sessions were a restrained alternative to carousing on the town. Everybody smoked in that era but there was never any mention or consideration of other drugs.

My career direction at the outset was somewhat haphazard for lack of formulated objectives. Vivid memories remain of interesting courses and stimulating teachers, but where this knowledge would lead was pretty nebulous. I started out with a major in economics to broaden my base and shifted to zoology in my junior year. An important aspect of my education resulted from the good fortune to be accepted into the relatively small Naval ROTC program, which included such courses as engineering, navigation and seamanship. A highly desirable and very interesting adjunct to that program was the required summer cruises to Hawaii on battleships and to Alaska on a destroyer. It was an enjoyable supplement to standard academics and one which proved useful when the war started.

My on-campus social career was unspectacular. I had neither the drive nor the talent for wheeling and dealing. As a freshman my negligent attitude about the fraternity's requirement to participate in some extracurricular campus activity resulted in another corporal discipline at the end of the academic year. When I asked what they wanted me to do, someone made the casual suggestion that since I was tall, why not try out for crew. Thus in my sophomore year, I dutifully signed up and began the arduous training with the freshmen for a new learning process in the seemingly futile objective of competing on the varsity squad. I had absolutely no expectation—or even much ambition—for ascending from the bottom levels of the squad. And, of course, any aspirations to athletic glory in a sport that had brought international and Olympic fame to UC were furthest from my mind. My other campus activities eventually resulted in being elected to most of the important societies—including the prestigious Order of the Golden Bear. But I failed to be tapped for the most coveted senior drinking society, Skull & Keys, populated by the campus bigwigs. These activities along with the various social diversions were no impediment to my modest academic objectives. On the other hand, my involvement in competitive varsity rowing required a major commitment of time and energy that was detrimental to studying. It also made it difficult to fulfill the tasks of afternoon laboratory courses essential for the post-graduate possibilities that I had in mind. At the very least it was imprudent, and perhaps even stupid, to engage in an activity that would seriously threaten my career, particularly since it held no expectation of significant accomplishment. Fortunately, I was able to complete the courses but my 3.5 grade point average, even though it gained me the Crew Scholarship Award, was less than optimal to compete for any good graduate school. And as for the usual expectations of the leading medical schools, which were flooded with applicants in the near 4.0 grade average, my chances were almost pathetic.

Other distractions contributed to my mediocre performance. The presence of the opposite sex on campus provided plenty of encouragement to those surging hormones so naturally there was some dating. By the standards of the late twentieth century we were innocent lambs constrained by the remnants of Victorian mores. Sororities and women's dormitories had midnight curfews and sex was difficult to come by. There were, of course, many college romances that ultimately resulted in matrimony but absolutely no bisexual communal living, no illegitimate babies that we knew of and lots of frustration was the standard of the times.

All in all, my college career was enjoyable, educational, and rewarding, but not spectacular. I was satisfied with my general performance but it left me with no important sense of purpose and no great self-esteem. As I look back on it we were fortunate to have enjoyed great times and homogeneous contemporaries in an era devoid of affluence. Although we cer-

tainly did not fully appreciate the quality and impact of our academic surroundings, I have memories of colorful teachers, some of whom became
famous, and lots of interesting information that does not relate to my profession. It was a valuable foundation for what was to come and if I had it
to do it again there is little that I would choose to do differently. If anything, I would broaden the diversity of my curriculum and minimize its
scientific aspect, which proved to be of far less use than expected to be
when we got to medical school. A major defect of preparing for graduate
school was adequate emphasis on effective communication—both oral
and written. We should properly have been told and shown that knowledge and skill is virtually worthless without the ability to convey it. My
subsequent teaching career has revealed how appallingly few physicians
and scientists are capable of articulating their expertise sufficiently well to
gain the respect they deserve.

Significantly I later became a member of a small cadre of fifty odd
male classmates who had been the movers and shakers of our year that has
perpetuated our college identity at an annual luncheon faithfully attended
ever since World War II. Even though the dialog is limited to, "how are
you?", a few reminiscences, and some off-color jokes, there is a strong
undercurrent of a common identity with a cultural background, a strong
influence on our lives and pride in a respected institution despite the shift
of my interests and affiliations to a professional level. Members of this
group have garnished the friendships by hosting some delightful parties
for our joint 70th and 80th birthdays but the big class reunions have been
disappointing.

CHAPTER 5

Why Rowing?

Since my lack of athletic talent had been established before starting college it was hardly to be expected that my career would be colored by involvement in a major sport. Thus it was significant and paradoxical that this non-academic aspect of college indirectly turned out to play a much bigger role in my academic, professional and domestic future than any part of my scholastic performance. Crew, under the coaching of spectacularly successful Carroll "Ky" Ebright, significantly altered the course of my life. Ironically getting into this activity was fortuitous as described above. Indeed it was almost ridiculous to fulfill a vague social requirement by choosing an activity whose demands predictably would endanger my academic performance and future potential. Clearly I was absorbed in the number one priority of peer approbation and conveniently put the nebulous future on hold. Little did I realize that the consequence of this naive and foolish choice would become an asset rather than a liability. There were no high school crews in those days and the freshmen who aspired to be oarsmen started their rowing careers as neophytes by learning the tricky technique of how to pull an oar in a big, heavy flat-bottomed scow for more than a month to prepare for the real thing. As an equal neophyte I joined that exercise as a sophomore but when the others graduated together for their first encounter in narrow unstable shells on the freshman squad, I was necessarily shoved into the bottom of the seasoned varsity hierarchy, all of whom had at least a year of experience in eight-oared shells. Because the endeavor was undertaken under duress I could swallow my frustrations by rationalizing that it was at least useful and healthy to get some structured exercise and it did not occur to me to feel sorry for myself over the futility of the endeavor. With no realistic prospect of ever ascending from the cellar, I nevertheless was inherently conscientious and got caught in the competitive spirit to give it my best effort. An unlikely combination of luck, determination, and unexpected natural aptitude allowed me to survive the formidable competition of the eager varsity contestants and gradually to get moved up to the third shell of the six boat varsity squad. The sport was a fortuitous choice for my physical characteristics because I was never quick enough for most ball sports but I did have the capacity for honing a repetitive process to a fine point. While there was some satisfaction in developing a new skill and being part of a team, it was a grueling business to ride the rickety bus leaving the campus every afternoon at 4:00 P.M. all the way across Oakland to the boathouse to practice on the dismal and dirty Oakland Estuary. Often I returned too tired to study, and this with no expectation of reward or recognition. But we were at an age when peer pressure and conformity were paramount. Discomfort was an integral part of the indoctrination process and it was unmanly to avoid it, no matter how senseless.

The following year, as a junior, I persisted in this seemingly futile quest, though I did ascend the ladder high enough to be selected for the junior varsity (second boat) crew to row against Washington, our major rival, in Seattle. It was a glorious and enjoyable trip with a week of recreation and daily practice on beautiful Lake Washington. We were reasonably accomplished as novices but our performance culminated in a valiant effort that was not quite good enough for a win. As my first encounter with intercollegiate competition it was an exciting and gratifying experience. But college athletes are expected to "do or die" for their endeavor and on our return trip I committed the cardinal sin of saying philosophically that our excursion had been a pleasant and satisfying experience *despite* not winning. This heretical thought almost got me thrown off the train.

Despite that gaff, I remained with this high-spirited group, which had fortuitously found that unusual ingredient to make it click. Certainly its spiritual leader and spark plug was Jimmy Dieterich, our coxswain, but much credit must also go to Kirk Smith for his physical leadership as the stroke who set the magical pace and rhythm. They gave the boat a unique feel of motion and comfort that made it run smoothly enough—some told us—to look as good as or better than the varsity. We were buoyed by our performance and hence eager to redeem our loss to Washington by participating in the big Intercollegiate Rowing Association (IRA) Regatta at

Poughkeepsie, New York at the end of the season. Our confidence that we would give a good showing was not matched by the decision makers in the front office of the Athletic Department who declined to provide sufficient funds for the JV crew to be included on the trip; only the varsity and the freshmen were chosen to go. Our zeal to participate led to developing our own funding by organizing a lottery. We put on our three piece suits and spent most of a week in the City visiting the Montgomery Street offices of our parents' friends and prominent Cal alumni to sell ten dollar books of tickets. It was an arduous but interesting experience, which was successful in raising enough money to finance the big opportunity. At that juncture, of course, we were campaigning to finance our travel as the *junior* varsity. Then, on a Saturday morning, just three weeks before the scheduled departure for the east, Ky led the whole squad out almost to the mouth of the Oakland Estuary, lined us up and declared that we would race each other the 4+ miles back to the boathouse with appropriate handicaps. He started the 6th boat 15 or 20 seconds (my guess) before the 5th and another 15 or 20 seconds before the 4th and so on, leaving us JVs expecting to be given the same start over the varsity. As we apprehensively watched the 3rd boat disappear almost out of sight, he casually picked up his megaphone and said, "Whoever gets to the boathouse first will be the varsity, GO!" What an unexpected thrill it was to be suddenly anointed as a viable challenger to the first boat. Our successful lottery had assured us a trip to the Regatta on the Hudson so we had nothing to lose and pure glory to win. We rowed our hearts out with all the spirit and energy we could muster. It was enormously rewarding to feel the exhilarating sensation of running so smoothly that the adrenaline made it seem almost effortless. Our subordinate expectations notwithstanding, it was not really surprising to find that we could hold our own against the varsity and exciting to find ourselves pulling steadily and progressively ahead. At the finish we had a lead of more than two boat lengths over what—up to that moment—had been the varsity. What an exalting triumph it was to acquire their mantle on the brink of departing for the big regatta! For me—such an unlikely participant in that athletic glory—it was unreal.

In the brief interval before we left for the east, Ky experimented extensively to seek the best available combination of oarsmen by shifting segments of the erstwhile varsity with their counterparts in the newly crowned crew. He spent several days bringing the boats together on the water to swap individuals, pairs and different groups of four (bow 4, stern 4 and middle 4) to satisfy himself that the new varsity was really the best crew. The spirit of what we had dubbed the "Club JV" prevailed. Except for two changes in the original JV, that crew went on to race the six other varsity crews on the Hudson River in June of 1938. The trip was an exciting adventure, starting with loading our shells, oars, equipment and launch into a railroad baggage car that would accompany the train we took across the country. Two members of the squad who did not make the cut elected to stow away in the launch for four miserably hot days, during which their sustenance was smuggled into the baggage car by their colleagues. The squad occupied a whole Pullman car, which was tacked on the rear of the Southern Pacific's train, *The Challenger*. Without air conditioning it was a hot trip in mid-June, but any discomforts were offset by the excitement of adventure and potential glory. We had separate and hearty meals with specially printed menus in the dining car and soft drinks in our private Pullman.

Our isolation at the end of the train permitted the casual atmosphere of a locker room to dress in the aisle and to cope with the hot weather by sleeping in the nude. During the last night out of Chicago, unbeknownst to us, two Pullman cars were added onto the train behind us. Our awakening the next morning was accompanied by the usual disgorging of thirty odd naked bodies into the aisle. At the moment when one hairy oarsman had emerged from his upper berth by reaching across to the opposite bar to hang spread-eagled and another had his butt up in the air to reach for his bag under the seat, the rear door opened to reveal two women school teachers on their way to the dining car. I shall long remember their shocked expressions and screeches as they hastily retreated.

Our travels detoured to Ithaca, New York, where we had been invited to have a preliminary race against the Cornell crews on Lake Cayuga. This interlude provided an interesting and enjoyable experience which served to test the competitive performance of the new varsity. It was a happy day for the Cal squad because all three of our boats, freshman, JV & varsity, were victorious without significant challenge and our varsity broke a course record in the process. That proved to be the first of broken records on every course that crew undertook over two years and set the stage for the big Regatta. The final leg of the trip was on the New York Central tracks that approached the big city from the north.

The practice week on the Hudson River was memorable. Each college

(California, Cornell, Columbia, Navy, Princeton, Syracuse, & Washington) had its own boathouse and wharf just north of the town. The regatta teams had many curious and friendly visitors among whom was the local Sheriff, who was an avid Cal fan, promising us good luck by the legendary ceremony of rubbing his left testicle during the race. We were royally cared for by an excellent chef, who provided us with 4000 to 5000 delicious calories a day, and a trainer who gave us massages every night. We rowed twice a day in various patterns of sprint starts, long work-outs, and casual trials, one of which was to do the whole 4 mile course under full steam. It was a good performance and spies, of course, were timing us so our reputation became that of a favorite but Ky rapidly dissuaded us of any inclination to believe such nonsense. The hot, muggy weather was anathema to cool weather Northern Californians and it seemed to sap our strength but we gradually got used to it enough to be in good shape as the big day approached. When the race day arrived, our facade of casual confidence gave way to tension. We had to sit around the boat house for hours watching the freshman crew depart and anxiously awaiting the result of their race. Then the same for the JV, before finally suiting up and putting our boat in the water. The mile and a half row out to the starting line got us limbered up but was psychologically exhausting. The starting line consisted of seven anchored stake-boats, each containing a man to grasp a rudder, which he released at the gun. We had to maneuver by backing up against the current to get in position.

I do not remember the details of that race except for getting a good start and gradually pulling ahead of Washington, our arch rival, who had beaten us two months previously on their home waters. Four miles is a grueling distance and stamina was a big factor that may have favored the western crews with longer outdoor training seasons, who had dominated that regatta for several years. The rest of the pack seemed to be behind Washington and we maintained a comfortable lead against what we thought to be all challengers to cross the finish line with an apparent gratifying victory. However, we were shocked to recognize that the finish line was long and slanted, at the other end of which Navy's shell had sneaked passed us unnoticed to cross in a photo finish six feet ahead of us. It was a crushing disappointment to have victory snatched from our grasp. From my standpoint, however, it was a most exciting experience to have participated in a great regatta and to row a good race, in which the disappointment of not winning was partially assuaged by the fact that *both* we and Navy had broken the course record. I felt quite satisfied.

That juncture I assumed to be the pinnacle—and the end—of my athletic career. With more glory, recognition and satisfaction than I had ever remotely expected and with the prospect of medical school ahead plus an unfulfilled requirement of a summer Navy cruise, I presumed it was time to hang up my oar and think about more important things. The experience had been rewarding and its extra bonus was to transport me across the country where I had the opportunity to visit and be interviewed at eastern medical schools, which otherwise would certainly have been unattainable. Indeed it turned out to be a determinant of my career for which I have always remained most grateful. But the time had come to buckle down and obtain the necessary credentials for acceptance at a first class graduate school. I had somehow managed to maintain a reasonably good academic record but the time and energy expended on crew had taken its toll. But again the tyranny of expectation thwarted my attempt to break out of the mold. When crew training began the following spring I became a susceptible victim of peer pressure by being cajoled and shamed into not being a quitter so I relented reluctantly and reported for practice. It was probably imprudent of me to have undertaken rowing in the first place but at this juncture it was even more foolhardy to risk fulfilling important laboratory courses and a respectable academic record. Confirmation and compounding of that folly emerged early in the training season when my achievement and recognition of the previous year were demolished by a progressive demotion to the 3rd and even the 4th boat where the smoothness was absent and the fun was gone. It is true that the coach would occasionally bring his launch over from its usual position next to the varsity and shout at me to "pull harder" but I failed to recognize the significance of those gestures and became very discouraged. I sensibly decided that it was time to defect before exposing my chagrin at the occasion of the final practice session before the big Washington race with its fanfare of new uniforms, new oars, and press coverage. Naturally, I had some feelings of disappointment but I do not recall any resentment or sense of failure. I was philosophical about changing times and appreciative of my prior good fortune. My unintended rowing career had already far exceeded my expectations and I thought was behind me, probably for the best.

But it was not to be so. That night I got phone calls from Jimmy

Dieterich, our coxswain, and Kirk Smith, the stroke, prevailing on me not to be a sorehead and insisting that I show up the next day. I almost ignored their pleas but did come to the boat house prepared to hide in the background. I saw no purpose in changing my clothes but someone cajoled me into doing so. Ky made his various announcements to the gathered squad with reporters lurking in the background and then read off the names of those who had been chosen to race against Washington; first the freshman crew, then the JV crew, and finally the varsity. Positions, by tradition, were called off starting with the coxswain, then stroke,7,6,5,4,3,2,bow. All of the names I heard were those who had been in their positions for days or weeks. Even the varsity list began with crew that had been rowing together for weeks, nearly all of which were from the preceding year's varsity. The sequence was consistent all the way down to the last name which seemed certain to be the man who had been rowing in my seat. At that instant I wished I had stayed home to be spared the disappointment of being the only exception. Then I heard "Bow: Roe." What a shock! It was a ridiculous dream sequence from which I expected to wake up. To this day I have no idea what went through Ebright's mind because he acted as if it were a foregone conclusion that I would be on the varsity and left me to infer that my stint "in the pits" was just to keep me from getting cocky.

It was a marvelous feeling to be back in the varsity boat with the camaraderie of my old teammates, the same 1938 crew with only one replacement, and to appreciate even more the comfortable and indefinable feeling of a smoothly running boat. Every stroke had rhythm and momentum that promised to provide a championship performance. The big mid-season three mile race against Washington, our strongest rival, was a triumphant victory on the Oakland estuary with a record breaking twelve-length lead, going away. A couple of weeks later we went on to Long Beach for a substantial and record breaking victory against UCLA in a 2000 meter sprint. In the post-race ceremony of throwing the coxswain in the water a press photographer happened to catch me appearing to be walking on water (Fig 1.). In June we again crossed the country by train to the IRA at Poughkeepsie. The trip was, as always, interrupted by a change of trains in Chicago with a layover of a few hours. Rather than turn us loose to get into trouble in the windy city it was arranged to have a practice row at Lincoln Park on Lake Michigan. The only available eight-oared shell was rigged for the stroke oar on the starboard side instead of the usual port side configu-

ration. This resulted in my being shifted from bow to stroke and moving all
the others up. It was the only occasion on which I was the pacesetter and
it lasted only an hour or so, but I remember that unique experience with
pleasure and with amplified respect for the responsibilities of the stroke.

Again we had a strenuous but enjoyable week of training and pleasant summer leisure along Boathouse Row, which was a suitable build-up for
the big race day. This year we were considered by the press to be the
favorites and therefore got even more attention than the year before. Our
group picture was printed in the *New York Times* but it had been taken with
all of us bare chested so the editor had white jerseys airbrushed on. How
prudish could he be?

As we rowed out to the stake boats at the start, even though I had
been there before and done the race without difficulty, I remember looking
down the river at the bridge three and a half miles away —a half a mile
short of the finish line. It seemed an impossible distance and I was terrified
at the prospect of not making it. That terror was reinforced during the first
five minutes of the race in which I became utterly exhausted and certain
that I would collapse. But then I got my second wind and the boat settled
down to its comfortable feel. Our coxswain Jimmy Dieterich shrewdly
drove us to an optimal performance and carefully evaluated our substantial
lead over the field of seven varsity "8's" as we began the last half mile. The
water had become very choppy, which increased the risk of "catching a
crab" (submerging an oar) and losing out, so Jimmy elected to maintain our
slow and steady pace of 32 to 34 strokes a minute despite a determined
threat by Washington, this time our only serious contender. In their desperation to catch us they stepped up their pace to 40+, which succeeded in
closing the gap to put their bow just overlapping our stern. Most of us were
eager to match their challenge and maintain our lead but Jimmy and Kirk
Smith, the stroke, resisted our pleas and elected to maintain our comfortable pace thus allowing our lead to dwindle to half a length at the finish
line without calling on the customary big final effort that we were expecting. We therefore finished in stride and could easily have kept going for
another mile while some of the other crews collapsed over their oars in
exhaustion. It was a triumphant victory that made up for the preceding
year's disappointment, particularly because we had avenged Navy and
again established a new four-mile record of 18:12.6. That record still stands
today because the Poughkeepsie venue was abandoned after World War II

and the IRA cut down the four mile distance to three miles.

It was exhilarating to hear the whistles and horns that greeted our victory, particularly in memory of the preceding year when we had been dismayed to discover our defeat from the loud whistle of the Navy destroyer anchored at the finish. This year it was a big disappointment to miss the glory and celebration of the following evening but I had to make a hasty departure immediately after the race. Having failed to take my required Naval ROTC cruise to Alaska because of the previous year's regatta I was allowed to attend my graduation ceremony but was handed a blank scroll, withholding both my degree and Navy commission until that requirement was fulfilled. Thus my presence at this regatta was contingent on meeting the destroyer in Seattle to complete the cruise with the Class of '40, so I had to catch a plane to get there in time. It turned out to be an interesting and educational trip—even if an anticlimax to athletic glory—and I returned home to direct my attention to preparing for the dramatic change of venue to start medical school in Boston.

This sequence of events resulted in two subsequent surprises: First, was to learn about the forgotten and unseen press coverage of the race several months later when my mother presented me with a scrapbook of photos and clippings. Only then did I realize that the New York Times reporter had written that ours was the best crew that had ever been seen on the river and another report predicted that our record would stand for fifty years (It has now stood for sixty years.) The second surprise occurred almost thirteen years later when we returned to San Francisco and walked into a rented apartment to be greeted by my oar mounted in the entrance hallway. By tradition, every crew member who won at Poughkeepsie was allowed to keep his oar, and my father had told me that he had collected mine while I was away at medical school, but I had completely forgotten about it. That twelve-foot-long "ornament" has followed us ever since.

For one who could hardly be described as a jock I must acknowledge that rowing provided enduring rewards beyond the satisfaction of winning. It brought me into a world that I never would have known and had never aspired to. It enhanced my physical state and taught me the fascinating psychology of athletic competition, the amazing potential of human endurance and the unique exhilaration of being a champion. Rowing represents the epitome of a cooperative effort in a skill that few observers understand. Whatever satisfaction it provides is necessarily communal because success is measured for the whole with no individual glory. It was truly no place for a maverick and contradicts my underlying philosophy. Nevertheless it must have been important for me to give it my best; otherwise how can I account for the cliff-hanging scenario of that last early season training in the cellar of recognition? Persistence has played an important role in my career.

This episode in my life disappeared into limbo during the pursuit of a professional career and not until forty years later did I fully appreciate the significance of that experience. Our 1939 University of California Crew was belatedly inducted into the Rowing Hall of Fame in 1979. All of us arrived in Seattle for this delightful occasion, which also was a posthumous tribute to Ky Ebright. This remarkable coach had produced 3 Olympic Championship crews. (Had the 1940 Olympics not been canceled by World War II he had hoped our crew might give him a 4th). We were told that their prior presence in the Hall of Fame had given U.C. an overbalanced representation, which kept putting off the nomination of our '39 crew despite its records. Ky lived long enough to learn of our acceptance and only then did he tell the press that the '39 Crew was the best one he had ever coached. This same crew was reunited ten years later for a fiftieth anniversary and, after weighing in *under* our graduation weights, rowed two miles together on the estuary. All of us were most appreciative of our association and of the inspiration we received from a remarkable coach.

Absent this frosting on my otherwise unspectacular academic credentials it is reasonably certain that I was no likely contender for a top flight medical school with a B+ grade average as my only qualification. And my being on the east coast for the 1938 Regatta made it possible to be interviewed at schools like Columbia, Cornell, Pennsylvania, and Johns Hopkins, as well as Harvard. Almost certainly my family would not have sponsored such a trip at that time. My patron grandmother Laura Story even resisted my going to Harvard after being accepted because she thought the schools in California were "quite good enough."

Another member of our rowing entourage, who was selected to be a substitute, also took advantage of being transported to the east coast to initiate his career. He was a classmate who had aspirations as an actor and went to Connecticut after the race to engage in Summer Stock. We knew him as Eldred Peck, later to be known as Gregory, and to become by far the must illustrious personality of our era.

CHAPTER 6

Backing Into Harvard Medical School

While some choose a career by virtue of family tradition, childhood dreams or perceived interests, I had doubts about what I wanted to be, what kind of living I could make, and my capabilities for success. My father's career of disappointments reflected resentment at being steered into engineering because of his father's fortuitous success with the electric dynamo. He did have a keen interest in scientific things and I am convinced that he had always wished he had been a doctor. But certainly he never tried to influence me in that direction, or any other. He left me to make up my own mind.

Thus, I undertook the adventure of college with no clear purpose but with the hope that an opportunity would develop. Although I avoided a science major to cut as broad a swath through the curriculum as possible, the potential of a medical career as an outlet for my perceived interest in science was lurking in the back of my mind. So I tiptoed through a few of the basic courses in chemistry and zoology, just in case. But I deliberately avoided the standard pre-med curriculum, partially because of its distasteful reputation for vicious competition, and principally because it required the fourth undergraduate year to overlap with the first year of medical school. This meant moving to the San Francisco campus after only three years in Berkeley, which would have obviated all the social pleasures of senior year on campus and would have disqualified me for the Naval ROTC program. And, as it turned out, my rowing experience would have been impossible. Having the extra year of college and avoiding the high pressure concentrated course allowed me to broaden my education and improve my perspective. The streamlined pathway was later abandoned by all medical schools for that very reason. Incidental courses that occupied this intellectual cushion included architecture, anthropology, astronomy, economics, music appreciation, and English, all of which have led to subsequent pleasurable interests and important perspectives outside of medicine. My only regret was not to have taken even more non-science courses. In particular I subsequently recognized the great importance of English in mastering the art of communication, without which it is difficult to be effective in any field. Indeed, I have campaigned as a member of the medical school faculty to encourage undergraduates to minimize their biology courses and emphasize their humanities courses. Acceptance of that approach has slowly gained ground at many medical schools.

Whether and when to make a definitive step to establish a career would remain uncertain up to the last minute. Thoughts about medical school remained but without commitment. The triggering factor was when I recognized the fortuitous importance of being in New York after the crew race in the summer of my junior year. I looked at the prominent eastern medical schools and developed a background for filing applications when the occasion presented itself a few months later. My Uncle Dick Bertheau, the New York banker, invited me to stay with him after the 1938 Regatta to pursue this project and I remain eternally grateful to him for taking an interest in my quest. He arranged introductions that I would not have otherwise known how to pursue. Fortuitously, one of my two interviewers at Columbia Medical School was Dr. Fordyce B. St. John, who was destined to become my father-in-law seven years later.

The New York venue, however, turned out to be a pathway elsewhere. Uncle Dick invited to dinner a nice gentleman he introduced as his personal physician. This doctor graciously showed an interest in my career direction and suggested that I take a look at a "real" medical school, whereupon he picked up the phone, called a friend in Boston, wrote an address on his card and told me to get on the 7:00 A.M. train. That excursion took me to the office of another charming gentleman at the Peter Bent Brigham Hospital who took me in tow for several hours of his busy schedule, sent me to meet the dean at Harvard, and personally drove me back to the train station. It was a delightful and fascinating experience, the significance of which I was totally unaware. Of course that episode played an important role in my future, but it was not until some time later that I recognized *how* fortunate I had been. The "nice gentleman" at Dick's apartment was not just a personal physician but Dr. Frank Berry, a Harvard Medical graduate and one of New York's most prominent and influential surgeons, later to be appointed Assistant Secretary of Defense, in charge of all military medical affairs during World War II. (It was my great privilege that he also became my life long mentor and friend.) And the "nice gentleman" in Boston was Eliot Carr Cutler, internationally renowned professor of surgery at Harvard and later head of military medicine in the European Theater during World War II. These fortuitous introductions undoubtedly were crucial influences on my acceptance at Harvard. The plethora of straight A applicants to that school allowed the dean of admissions to diversify his selections to encompass other accomplishments. Had I achieved a nearly perfect academic record in Berkeley instead of going out for crew it would have been futile—even preposterous—to apply for Harvard.

Of course the process was not as simple as retrospect makes it seem. Harvard had more than sixteen applicants for every place in the class, which should dampen the expectations of even outstanding students. But I was unaware of those odds and remained hopeful. When acceptances began to arrive from other top flight schools like Columbia, Cornell, and Pennsylvania, all wanting prompt replies, I was faced with the agonizing alternative of either recognizing that Harvard was unlikely and accepting a close-to-first choice before the offer expired, or of risking the hope that a favorable letter would arrive from Boston. As luck would have it the acceptance to Harvard did arrive just in the nick of time and was one of my life's moments of triumph, which I had no justification to expect and little appreciation of how fortunate I was. That my family could see fit to underwrite my expenses was also no small miracle.

My first thoughts were understandably concentrated on the pride and satisfaction of attaining the most highly respected medical school in the country, perhaps the world. But it soon dawned on me that the competition would probably be over my head and the prospect made me apprehensive. On meeting my classmates it was at first deceiving to find a group of nice guys with little of apparent distinction. No one talked much about himself. Phi Beta Kappa keys were a dime a dozen but they rapidly disappeared as we took on a non-hierarchical presence. Eventually, it emerged that the group had a range of exceptional talents and remarkable accomplishments. I was delighted and privileged to be one of them and even if I might not be up to their performance it was a hopeful gamble that the fall-back would not be too traumatic. The class, we were later to find out, was exceptional even for Harvard's high standards. These men were to be my closest and most respected friends for the rest of my life.

In the retrospect of sixty years this was an interesting experience that turned out to be far less stressful and more pleasurable than I would have expected. The atmosphere was fraternal with a roster of wide geographic and institutional diversity (30+ colleges), but with virtually no ethnic or gender diversity. We lived in a comfortable dormitory with maid service and we ate our excellent meals served by waitresses in an attractive dining hall. Three-piece suits and ties were worn to class every day. Boston is a delightful city with countless diversions in which we all indulged: symphony, theater, museums, restaurants, and nightclubs as well as delightful environs to which we were often invited. Beaches were nearby and skiing was only a three or four hour drive. It is a wonder that any of us could concentrate on our studies.

The Harvard Mystique

It is said that "you can always tell a Harvard man, but you can't tell him much." This reflects a disdain for the Harvard graduate who displays arrogance. I had considered this affect to be unwarranted and unattractive until my curmudgeonly friend Mark Ravich from Johns Hopkins wrote a compelling essay on arrogance, in which he adroitly identifies the surgeon's initiative and acceptance of responsibility as a manifestation of arrogance. [iv] This approach fits neatly into the feelings I have derived from my association with Harvard. Yes, Harvard men, and more recently women, do tend to be arrogant but perhaps some have also been inculcated with a sense of responsibility.

When I arrived at the Harvard Medical School, young, naive, bewildered and with only the vaguest career objectives I was, as I mentioned, frightened by the daunting prospect of keeping up with the awesome competition, but the Dean's official greeting on the first day was reassuring. He told us we had been selected from more than 1700 applicants with complete confidence that all of us were capable of being good doctors and that the faculty was committed to getting us there. [This message was in sharp contrast to the custom at the Harvard Law School where the large admitting class was told: "Look to the man on your left and look to the man on your right; only one of you will be here after Christmas."]

Not long after our indoctrination, I recognized an undertone, never specifically articulated, that we had become part of an institution with world-wide influence and that it would not suffice for us to be just physicians, no matter how skilled. We are expected to be responsible leaders and contributors academically, professionally and/or socially. That charge, subtle though it was, has certainly been fulfilled. At its twenty-fifth reunion our class, with 120 survivors, accounted for ten academic department chairmen, twenty four full professors, thirty-eight associate and assistant professors, one university president (Amherst), and dozens of community hospital chiefs of staff, chiefs of service, community leaders and professional moguls.

This identity was not just a product of our academic diligence in medical school. Indeed our life was one of pleasant collegiality. Nearly everyone lived in the Vanderbilt Hall dormitory because almost none were married. Our meals were served at open tables in the dining room and there was a late evening snack bar as a gathering point to interrupt our studies. There was much social intercourse that indulged our time between the hours of study. The school had a policy of issuing no grades unless one was threatened with failure, the result of which created a mutual objective without competitiveness. These indulgences were immensely valuable, both socially, because lasting relationships were developed, and intellectually since much of the conversation was about our courses and our work. My academic survival was significantly supported by bits of information acquired during meals. The most dramatic example of that pathway was at the breakfast table preceding our final examination in Anatomy. A "smart ass" sat down and smugly asked the group if anyone knew the collateral circulation of the liver, which *Gray's Anatomy* described in a fine print footnote that most of us had skipped over without realizing its clinical importance. He obliged us with a recitation of the anatomy, which most of us considered to be esoteric. Alas, it appeared as one of the main questions on the exam and I was able to pass only because of what I could recall from the breakfast dissertation. This attitude of sharing knowledge with fellow students was in sharp contrast with the behavior at U.C. Medical School where my college colleagues reported that every bit of information was jealously husbanded in a quest for competitive advantage.

All of us complied with the academic expectations of a graduate school but to differing degrees of diligence. There was a tennis court in the center yard and a gymnasium with a basketball court and eight squash courts, all of which were kept very busy, usually until the lights went off at 10:30 p.m. I played squash literally every day of my four years in Vanderbilt Hall. There was an active choral group; a scientific group, The Boylston Medical Society, the oldest medical society in America; two fraternities; two senior social clubs; all of which provided either recreational or intellectual diversion. A group of us had a poker game every Thursday night. Week ends were frequently punctuated with cocktail parties and/or random excursions into the country. It was a thoroughly enjoyable period, which I have frequently acknowledged would have been one of the brightest four years of my life even if I had flunked out a week before graduation and never practiced medicine.

Those pleasures and friendships have perpetuated over the years by maintaining contacts during our numerous visits to Boston for a variety of medical meetings. It was also my subsequent good fortune to be elected to a three year term on the Alumni Council, which met at the school three times a year and played an active role in academic and administrative affairs. Most particularly we have derived enormous pleasure and interest by attending each of our five-year Medical School reunions starting at the twenty-fifth and ending most recently with our fifty-fifth in 1998. These beautifully orchestrated occasions have each consisted of a Wednesday night dinner or social event with our classmates, an interesting and variegated scientific program and luncheon on Thursday at the Medical School, and a Class Day ceremony on Friday with amusing talks followed by luncheon on the quadrangle. Friday afternoon everyone took off for a purely recreational weekend at some resort on the North Shore, Cape Cod, Narragansett Bay, Martha's Vineyard, or Nantucket—each with a hotel reserved for the exclusive use of two reuniting classes. It is nearly impossible to come away from these events without the strongest, warmest, and proudest possible identification with both classmates and the school.

If my enthusiasm seems a bit excessive it must be seen in the context of a naïve western boy who, up until coming to Boston, had never been totally comfortable with his social and intellectual surroundings, had never lived with a large group of what he considered to be his peers, and had never felt totally accepted. Harvard is where I found it all for the first time. The unique aspect of that relationship was amusingly punctuated at our fortieth reunion which was billeted on Nantucket Island along with the class of '58—fifteen years our junior. On the ferry ride out to the island there was a slight air of resentment by the younger group that their fun might be spoiled by the old fogies. All turned out to be pleased that the weekend was a great success for both groups as we played and gathered, either together or separately. Returning on the ferry Sunday afternoon I was accosted by a group from the '58 class who wanted to know why it was clearly evident that our class had an even better time than they did. On reflection I realized that we were much closer knit because ours was a smaller class, who were raised during the Depression, very few were married and we lived out of each other's pockets for four intense years, punctuated by the start of World War II. These circumstances established an intimacy that was not likely to be matched in a group that was larger, more heterogeneous, most of whom were married and lived off campus. Clearly the post-war classes shared our sense of pleasure and satisfaction as alumni but probably with less intensity.

Throughout the four years of medical school I retained a sense of academic insecurity from being surrounded by overtly bright classmates, though by surviving I gradually gained confidence among my peers. We were never told about our academic performance and there were times when I felt inadequate, genuinely doubtful that I would make it through. There was no reason to believe that I might be excelling. Thus I was mystified by a visit one evening near the end of our third year by a couple of seniors who had to wait for me to finish the hand in a poker game before informing me of their purpose to tap me for AOA (Alpha Omega Alpha), the medical school counterpart of Phi Beta Kappa. This was such a total surprise that I was certain they had made a mistake. It was my first inkling that I might have a promising career and a prelude to an invitation to take the oral examinations for graduation honors, which was an interesting experience that I found to be enjoyable because its significance was lost in being too unreal to worry about. Even though I missed the commencement ceremony by taking a brief holiday in Florida before starting my internship I am pleased to have a *cum laude* on my diploma.

It was equally surprising to be elected to the Aesculapian Club, an exclusive philanthropic society whose sixteen initiates are the senior students who produce the annual play. This frequently ribald faculty roast consumed a great deal of talent and time before its two performances, a dress rehearsal at the senior class dinner, and the big show to the faculty at the club meeting. My musical and thespian talents are sparse so my role in the production was minimal, but it was certainly a lot of fun to be part of a successful and amusing show with a group of colorful, talented contemporaries who were to become my closest lifetime friends.

I have remained supportive and loyal to Harvard and proud to be identified with its image of leadership. It provided new aspects to my life in a stimulating atmosphere, a culture that I had never known, durable friendships with interesting and outstanding people, inspiration from brilliant and colorful teachers, plus a strong identity with a pursuit of excellence. Although these treasures have evoked considerable satisfaction, most of us carried away a stronger sense of responsibility, a mandate to provide leadership and an obligation to accomplish something worthwhile with our blessings. It was Harvard's creed that spawned my subsequent dedication to promoting higher standards of professional behavior and performance throughout my career.

Attendance at HMS was a leg up for obtaining a desirable internship and I was optimistic on the basis of the dean's encouragement. But still it was very good news to learn that my first choice application to the Surgical Service at Massachusetts General Hospital (MGH) had been accepted. That service usually took only six interns per year but the war had caused an exodus to the military, which required restructuring the training program, and they took sixteen surgical interns from our class with the recognition that the military draft would allow certain deferral for only a truncated nine month internship. At that time, typical surgical training around the country consisted of only two years of hospital internship. This was either on a service treating charity patients, associated with minimal teaching or supervision, or as an apprentice to a practicing surgeon, which provided a variable range of guidance and experience. There were less than two dozen hospitals in the U.S. and probably in the world that had espoused the pattern of tightly supervised graduated training extended over six or seven years established at Johns Hopkins by William Halsted. The MGH had been one of the first to espouse this elite policy, thereby making its appointments coveted.

CHAPTER 7

The Gauntlet of Surgical Training

The most challenging, difficult and strenuous period in a physician's life is the internship and residency between medical school and practice. The hours are long, demands extreme, stresses high, and the responsibilities great. The training is an ordeal from which we derived intensive learning by working under pressure and performing under critical supervision. All clinical training is strenuous but in surgery the load is compounded by the long hours and sometimes exhausting physical demands in the operating room, in addition to patient care, technical procedures, work-up, and clerical responsibilities of a non-surgical service. During this period, we had our initiation into the responsibilities of being a "real doctor" and the satisfaction of doing something tangible to cure disease, but it was all under the apron of a tightly organized team.

When I began surgical training at the MGH these generalities were compounded by the psychological impact of holding an appointment which had numerous qualified candidates waiting eagerly in the wings to take our places if we should stumble. Dedication was necessarily total—marriage was a disqualification before the war and those who got married got fired. Our unpretentious official title was "House Pupil."

An intern's day began at 5:00 A.M. to reach the ward laboratory in time to complete several urinalyses and blood counts and grab some breakfast before morning rounds began at 6:30. The chief resident would lead the full entourage of assistant residents, interns, medical students with the head nurse to sixty bedsides for informational reports, wound inspections, medication orders, management plans, and procedural assignments. His role was a cross between a czar and a drill sergeant. Woe to any underling who forgot, neglected, or failed to complete what he had been assigned. There were no excuses for the enormity of the workload or having to do emergency surgery during the night, or for the fact that some essential item to do the job was just unavailable.

Since doing surgery was our raison d'être we looked forward to the time in the operating room and eagerly awaited each step in our progression to being *the* surgeon. We started out as second assistants, holding retractors, often in awkward positions, and seeing at least part of the procedure, or as first assistant on relatively minor procedures. As we became first assistants we were allowed to perform more and more important parts of the operation. When we became the surgeon it was initially with supervisory help to prevent mistakes. Then we did it solo with an intern. Certainly our eagerness to operate exceeded our skill but it did seem an awfully long wait to get our wings. However, our degree of participation was enviable by comparison with other training programs where residents did little or no surgery until the final year of chief residency.

The war was going on during this period and the sixteen surgical interns were deferred from the military draft only for nine months. At the end of that period, I was lucky to be one of the four who were selected to stay for a second nine months, which resulted in another deferral from active military service and enough additional experience to be useful as a medical officer. However, there was a cloak of guilt in forsaking a patriotic duty, not to mention a moral obligation to the Navy for my four years of training in college and my commission in the Naval Reserve. Henry Moorman and I established a pact that we would leave for the war after that second appointment. However as that date approached we were both selected to stay for a third deferral, which he accepted and I declined. It was a difficult choice to forsake such a valuable training opportunity and perhaps to jeopardize my chances of being able to return after the war. But my conscience prevailed and my orders to active duty arrived soon thereafter.

This interlude of active military service, which was the fate of all but the physically disabled of my generation, was of greater benefit to some than to others. Those partially trained surgeons who were attached to hospitals had significant clinical experience with trauma, while others, such as myself, had very little surgical activity at their duty assignment.

Little did we appreciate the rarity of our opportunity as MGH residents as compared to our counterparts everywhere else in the world who waited through years of apprenticeship and slow development of a practice without guidance before acquiring even a fraction of the first hand experience we were having every day. Nor did we realize that only a very few of the country's thousands of surgeons had received any training that approached either the quality or duration of that in the MGH program.

Our day-to-day mentor and disciplinarian was the chief resident on whose service we happened to be assigned. Needless to say these potential tormentors stood tall in our lives, their commands and admonitions are often recalled decades later. Those under whom I served were all strong and interesting characters, each with a different message, but the most dynamically intimidating was Francis Moore (later to become the professor and chief of surgery at the Peter Bent Brigham Hospital). "Franny" was a powerful presence who ran his troops like a drill sergeant and you could literally feel his entourage approaching like a freight train. Gordon Scannell was soft spoken and persuasive without intimidation, but always a scholar with a subtle wit. Both Franny and Gordon have remained good friends and admired colleagues over the years. Other chief residents, whose leadership is indelibly remembered, include Addison Brenizer, Dean Crystal, Nate Munroe, Charles Mixter, Irad Hardy, and John Raker.

Edward D. "Pete" Churchill was the Chief of Surgery at MGH and the John Homan's Professor of Surgery at Harvard. He was serving with the Army in Europe when I started my internship in 1943, but he returned after the War and I remain indebted to him both for selecting me to come back and complete my training and for the organization of a superb program in which I was privileged to participate. Dr. Churchill was an innovative pioneer in thoracic surgery; he did the first staged pneumonectomy. But he was skeptical about heart surgery even though the pioneering work on the pump-oxygenator (heart-lung machine) was begun by John Gibbon in his department. One of the famous anecdotes about Pete Churchill was a bit of daring during a lung resection: a branch of the pulmonary artery had been clamped and was ready to be ligated when he paused and said that there were no recordings of the blood pressure in the pulmonary circuit, so he briefly removed the clamp to see and measure how high the blood spurted. This exemplified the kind of daring scientific curiosity that played an important role in the development of heart surgery.

The one occasion at which we saw the mighty and fearsome chief resident subdued was during the weekly ward rounds and service meeting conducted by the chief of service. Chief's rounds were like a captain's inspection on shipboard with careful scrutiny of the week's work. Patients were randomly selected by the chief for questions and/or critical commentary on some aspect of diagnosis or management. Surgical wounds were criticized, regimens reviewed, and management scrutinized. After an hour on the wards, the troops convened in a small library where the chief resident recited a list of all the week's operations and significant events for intensive review of each death and complication. The unbridled dialogue at these meetings imposed a heavy pressure on us to perform optimally and left no doubt about how things ought to be done. Every abnormal occurrence was examined with the attitude that someone might have erred and we must find out how; mistake was assumed until innocence was proven. Little did we appreciate the relative rarity of such candor and expectation until we learned that all other supposedly respectable institutions did not subscribe to similar standards. Not everyone enjoys the security of hanging out his dirty linen without risking disgrace, but doing it was a marvelously effective training tool.

Another weekly event was Grand Rounds at which the resident staff selected and presented interesting cases to a full auditorium with the senior attending surgeons in the front row. We would deliberately manipulate the information to create controversy, thus provoking lively and spontaneous discussion. One of my classmates, Henry Moorman, was a prankster who amused the gathering with bizarre props. To demonstrate the success of a hand operation, he wheeled in a piano for the patient to play a couple of bars of boogie woogie. On another occasion, Moorman obtained a suit of armor to demonstrate how to avoid contamination. Once, a patient who had fallen out of bed was wheeled in with a fish net wrapped around the bed. These sessions were popular not only for their clinical interest but also because of their spontaneity, controversy, and spots of humor. The show was entirely planned and orchestrated by the two chief residents, but its pace was guided by the unpredictable responses from the senior staff in the audience. We never knew whether a case would evoke lengthy discussion or silent acceptance, thus it was necessary to have prepared a long list of patients (with their x-rays, etc.) waiting in the corridor to avoid being empty-handed before the hour ended. The flip side of that precaution, of course, was that one or two—or even several—patients had been left to wait for an hour in a drafty corridor for naught.

One of the privileges of this rich experience was an intimate association with staff surgeons, not only in the course of our work but also in the doctor's dining room where we ate together. It is probable that I learned more in that venue than I did in the operating room, not to mention the pleasure of daily social and professional intercourse with so many distinguished personalities, many of whom invited us to their homes and remained life-long friends. Little did I appreciate this extremely valuable and enjoyable fringe benefit of my training period until some years later when this separate dining room was eliminated for economy reasons and these contacts ceased.

Of the Big Names we were admiring only Joe Meigs, chief of gynecology, was of Boston heritage and Oliver Cope was from Philadelphia, but all the others were unlikely mid-westerners: Arthur Allen from Kentucky, Pete Churchill from Illinois, Leland McKittrick from Wisconsin, and Claude Welch from Nebraska. That the MGH was a great institution could be attributed to the talent it attracted and the integrity it spawned in them rather than to its own heritage of historic New Englanders. The same, of course, can be said of the Harvard Medical School faculty, which had a small core of venerable Boston names, but the bulk of whom originated from all over the world.

There was no dearth of respect for the knowledge and skill of these mentors who were the essence of our training experience. I was also impressed with their integrity when it came to backing down from established positions particularly when the bad news derived from a lowly resident. None were small men who were driven to massaging their egos with authoritarian pressures. I remain grateful for that attribute when my first endeavor to complete a project involved a very controversial subject.

Pulmonary embolism (blood clot plugging the lung arteries) was a deadly postoperative complication that had captured the attention of Dr. Arthur Allen, our distinguished service chief, and others at the MGH who had become convinced of the preventive benefit of surgically dividing the big femoral vein in the groin for the least evidence of thrombophlebitis (clot formation) in the legs on the assumption that the pulmonary embolus had originated in the leg veins. They had written extensively and widely recommended this procedure, which was performed at the MGH with high frequency. However, during my six month stint in the Pathology Department, performing numerous autopsies, I noted that patients with pulmonary emboli seldom had evidence of leg phlebitis and conversely that femoral vein interruption had little influence on the outcome. I wrote a paper with Jerry Goldthwait on the statistics of this study, which significantly undermined this firmly established therapeutic doctrine. However, before submitting it for publication I consulted with both Dr. Allen and Dr. Linton, the leading proponents of what our paper refuted, who were dismayed by its message and who were influential enough to have it squelched. They reworked the data every way possible to reach a different conclusion, but to their credit they both ended up endorsing its submission. *The New England Journal of Medicine* accepted it for publication and it appeared as a lead article, presumably because of its heretical message.[*] It was my first publication and unintentionally turned out to be my first significant challenge to the establishment. Many thought it was political suicide to shoot down the local gospel and that I would never get appointed to the chief residency because of it. I was too naïve to recognize that hazard, which fortunately turned out to be a false concern.

One of the important strengths of that institution was the depth and variety of its staff. No individual or small group dominated the scene. Ideas, opinions, and practices were constantly under peer review and the system rapidly exposed anyone who tried to distort or exaggerate his results. Intellectual honesty prevailed because no one dared to distort it.

Time passed rapidly during the residency because we had little or no exposure to distractions and no money to spend on them anyway. My pay as an intern was zero (except for room and board); as an assistant resident it went up to $26/mo and later as a senior assistant resident $46/mo. And after 6 years of working up the ladder to the exalted position of chief resident, my pay was $100/mo. But we were proud of our role and pleased to be part of an elite fraternity, guided by some of the country's leading surgeons, and stimulated by a critical faculty who alerted us to every flaw in our performance. My residency at the MGH was the most distinctive and the most gratifying of all my institutional affiliations. Returning there from time to time for various occasions has evoked nostalgia for both events and personalities. It also evoked speculation over what my alternative fate might have been had I remained there to practice in what has long been one of the world's Meccas of surgery. I was devoted to its attitudes and practices and fond of the personnel with whom I had worked. Yet I was instinctively enough of a nonconformist that I would probably have been uncomfortable with the constraints that were imposed on the young faculty surgeons who waited for many years to develop any kind of practice within the feudal system and have a respectable income.

CHAPTER 8

Maverick Naval Officer—
An Oxymoron

Essential to survival in the armed forces, and especially in the Navy, is total obedience to authority, compliance with established protocol, and a firm adherence to the system. Anyone who veers from the conservative behavior pattern is destined for serious trouble, if not disgrace. It borders on the unbelievable that I managed to maintain an image of conscientious respectability during my active duty on a capital ship, the most formal and rigorous aspect of the Navy, while indulging myself with a subtle degree of non-compliance. This behavior emanated unconsciously from my natural inclinations, not from any overt intent to rebel or defy.

I had long been seduced by the so-called romance of the sea from my childhood reading and a minimal encounter with boats. Consequently, I was drawn to the glamour and seeming adventure of the Navy. As a high school student I thought seriously about applying to the Naval Academy but thankfully was persuaded that it was not a stimulating life time career. Nevertheless, I was interested on entering college to discover that there was a Naval ROTC program at Berkeley. The unit was small, elite, and competitively desirable because of its summer cruises to Hawaii and Alaska on warships. Because UC was a land grant university all male students, unless physically disabled, were required to take at least two years of Army ROTC program, which was generally considered an annoying chore. This necessity made Naval ROTC all the more attractive as an alternative.

By signing up for Naval ROTC, however, one committed to the full four year program and making graduation contingent upon completing all the requirements for receiving an Ensign's commission along with the university degree. Of course, the Navy was not interested in training a line officer who would eventually become a medical officer with no functions related to other military duties. It was necessary for me to register in a non pre-med major and to take an academic course that had no apparent medical intentions. This may appear deceitful but I had really not decided on my ultimate objectives, and was determined to have as broadly based an undergraduate education as possible, regardless of whether I would go to graduate school, and I was genuinely interested in the Navy. The ROTC program included courses in subjects that I would not otherwise have taken. Basic astronomy, spherical trigonometry, navigation, seamanship, aviation, and some engineering all proved to be interesting and would later turn out to be useful in a non-professional context. Parade ground drill in uniform was a weekly exercise for an hour that was not exactly fun but was mildly challenging. I managed to become company commander in my senior year and achieved embarrassing distinction at the year-end big parade ceremony by innocently striding about fifty feet ahead of my company as we passed the reviewing stand. Otherwise, my performance was one of reasonable conformity and mild academic distinction.

The program included three week summer training cruises. Freshmen and sophomores went to Hawaii on a battleship; one cruise was required and the second was optional. A cruise to Alaska on a destroyer was a requirement at the end of the junior year. These opportunities were particularly coveted during those Depression years when travel was a luxury that few could afford and a free trip to the Islands was an exciting prospect, even if marginally recreational. Each of these trips was interesting both for the desirable destinations and for the hands-on experience in gunnery, navigation, engineering, and seamanship. As cadets our situation was mixed. Our quarters and meals were as enlisted personnel. We slept in gun compartments on hammocks which had to be strung up at night and packed away at 5:00 A.M. reveille. We had no lockers so our clothes and possessions had to be stored in duffel bags. On the other hand we were treated to enjoyable social and recreational activities in various ports, the inhabitants of which were excited to be visited by a Navy ship and pleased to entertain nice college boys in uniform.

On our sophomore cruise, we eagerly anticipated the liberty excursion in Honolulu after completing a rigorous two-week training program. But this pleasure was dramatically terminated by a recall to the ship after hardly three hours ashore. The ship, the *U.S.S. Colorado*, was dispatched to the South Pacific to search for Amelia Earhart, whose plane had been lost in her round-the-world attempt. As history records, we were unsuccessful in that objective but the search took us to Johnston Island in the southern hemisphere. That resulted in our being subjected to the traumatic initiation ceremony associated with crossing the equator, known as a "Neptune Party."

For several days there were elaborate preparations for the occasion that included building a platform and creating a pool out of a wooden enclosure with a canvas lining on the forecastle. A hundred or more canvas shillelaghs were made by hand and filled with sand and sawdust. And there was much psychological hazing over the dire events to come.

When the fateful day arrived, on my nineteenth birthday, the uninitiated "pollywogs" were herded through an obstacle course on the forecastle consisting of well-orchestrated mayhem. It began with running nude, one at a time, down a hundred-foot gauntlet of perhaps forty equatorial veteran "shellbacks" flailing our buttocks with the aforementioned truncheons. Then we were force fed spoonfuls of some awful concoction like linoleum paste as a prelude to being thrust onto our knees in supplication to an enthroned and elaborately costumed King Neptune. This opportunity to disgorge the paste resulted in an electric shock to the coccyx that evoked a violent spasm, in the midst of which two or more stalwart sailors picked me up and threw me into a tank of sea water where more shellbacks administered a thorough, and seemingly almost fatal, ducking. Gasping for breath, I was rolled down a ramp from the far side of the tank to be grabbed and painted from head to foot with black fuel oil in preparation for the final gauntlet of a similar flailing down the other side of the forecastle. This whole nightmare probably took only a few minutes and nobody was injured, but it certainly was an ordeal. This ceremony of long maritime tradition was necessarily abandoned when the war started and then subsequent air travel created shellbacks by the thousands without any possibility of a ceremony so the custom seems to have died permanently. But I still keep the large ornate "official" certificate, signed by King Neptune, framed in my bathroom to document a memorable event and to remind me that I once was a hardy sailor.

On starting medical school, of course, all thoughts about the Navy were forgotten; that is until December 7, 1941, when my Sunday afternoon study session was interrupted with the news of the Pearl Harbor bombing. My status in the naval reserve required me to report forthwith to the Navy Headquarters in Boston. This I did with full expectation of ending or suspending my medical education and being called immediately to active duty. But despite my commission as a line officer and the Navy's urgent needs of the moment, I was told to go back and finish medical school. However they would not transfer me to the Medical Corps until I got my M.D. degree so I remained on twenty-four hour call and was required to be constantly available if needed. I graduated fifteen months later, did my internship plus at the MGH, and finally went to active duty as a Medical Officer in 1944.

In the brief interval between finishing my appointment at the MGH and reporting for active duty I drove my automobile across the country and deposited it with some belongings at home. While there, my parents gave a cocktail party that included some admiral, whose name I have forgotten but with whom I had a brief conversation about my initial assignment to the Hampton Roads Naval Air Station near Norfolk, Virginia. The admiral made a paternal suggestion that I drop in at the Bureau of Medicine and Surgery to register my preferences on my way through Washington. I almost laughed at him for what seemed to be a preposterous suggestion and I had no intention to comply with it. However when I later found myself in Washington with nothing better to do in a four hour layover before my train left for Norfolk, I reconsidered the idea and with a what-the-hell attitude I taxied over to the bureau. When the receptionist asked whom I wanted to see it was apparent that I was a lost soul. I felt ridiculous and turned tail for the exit. By chance a four-stripe captain happened to pass through the lobby at that moment and asked if he could be helpful. As I mumbled in embarrassed confusion he motioned me into his office and cordially informed me that he was in charge of assigning medical officers to their posts. When I told him of my destination he told me, as I already knew, that sea duty was soon in the offing. Then he pulled up my record and remarked about my school background, mentioning that he too was an HMS alumnus. When he asked me what I would like to have as sea duty I thought at first that he was joking because it was late in the war and none of my contemporaries had avoided being sent to remote stations, to minor ships or to the Fleet Marines. He left the room briefly and returned with two cards, announcing that I could choose between a cruiser and an aircraft carrier. In an incredulous daze I chose the cruiser and was told my orders to the USS *Philadelphia* would arrive in ten days. I thanked him and left in a state somewhere between euphoria and disbelief. Thus it was not surprising that my expectations were soon to be punctured.

I reported to the Naval Air Station at Hampton Roads where I was assigned a ward of forty patients, nearly all of whom were listed with a diagnosis of "Cat Fever." I was too embarrassed to acknowledge my ignorance of that disease and quickly retreated to the library, to no avail. Then I learned from a nurse that the term was Navy lingo for the flu (*catarrhal fever*).

A few days later while having cocktails in the officers club with some new-found colleagues, I casually related my experience at the bureau in Washington and my anticipation of duty on a cruiser. That was an indiscretion, provoking laughter and derision over my naiveté and gullibility. My optimism was crushed, and I felt chagrined to be in yet another role of an innocent freshman who had just been sold the Brooklyn Bridge. This disappointing news bruised my spirits for several days, even though my sense of realism told me that my expectations had been fantasy. But Lady Luck had not abandoned me. On the tenth day of my stint in the hospital my orders to the cruiser *did* arrive as promised. It was an exciting triumph and the last laugh was mine as I packed up to meet my ship in the Philadelphia Navy Yard.

That location and the ship's scheduled repair and retrofitting proved to be another stroke of fate because it was close enough to New York to follow up on a date with a wonderful girl whom I had met there a few months previously.

At the completion of our yard work, we embarked on a shake-down cruise to the Caribbean and then to North Atlantic patrol. Life at sea on a capital ship is quite comfortable even in wartime. We were well fed and I shared a small but adequate cabin with one other pleasant officer. The medical needs of 1500 healthy young men were minimal and my duties were far from demanding, so to alleviate the boredom I helped the navigating officer and ran the wardroom mess accounts.

The only mildly significant event of that duty was to take out an appendix in rough seas, which required my being strapped to the operating table and limited the available instruments to those my assistant and I could hold onto because everything else was thrown onto the deck. The captain obligingly altered the ship's course to minimize the motion but sent inquiries every ten minutes to ask if we were finished. The patient was unfazed by our difficulties and did well.

During this period, the war in Europe was intensifying with significant progress in driving back the Nazis. Our crucial supply line was still being attacked by German U-boats, which we were assigned to seek out and destroy. But just as we were headed across the Atlantic, V-E day was announced and we returned to Newport, Rhode Island for an exciting celebration. Jane came up from New York to stay with her sister Mary, whose husband John was on duty there. We had two glorious days of liberty together.

When I joined the ship there were two medical officers, of whom I was the junior, but the senior one was lazy, uninterested in practice and primarily cared about his social life. From my standpoint that was just fine because I became the ship's *de facto* physician and surgeon to benefit from whatever experience there was to be had. Later, after V-E Day, the other medical officer completed his service requirement and left active duty so I became the senior and only medical officer with a promotion in rank, raising my pay to $175/month.

Preparations were being made for the invasion of Japan and our ship was scheduled to be sent to the Pacific. That assignment, however, was postponed to be sent on an historical mission to escort the U.S.S. *Augusta* carrying President Truman to the famous meeting with Churchill and Stalin at Potsdam. With an admiral aboard, we were the flagship and protocol was more formal than usual, making unorthodox behavior especially unsuitable. Nevertheless, my casual attitude brought me to the brink of disaster one morning when I gave little thought to a stroll on deck around the forward turrets for some fresh air before lunch. In the process I unintentionally violated two cardinal rules of military behavior: being bareheaded and having my hands in my pockets. The result was a reprimand on the public address system from the bridge, "Will the doctor please get in the uniform of the day!" Knowing that the officer-of-the-deck at that moment was a friend who deprecated Navy formality I assumed he was pulling my leg so I casually replied by semaphore to "F-U-C-K Y-O-U."

Thirty seconds later, a Marine corporal appeared, did not make the customary salute, because without the symbolic cap I was not recognized as an officer, and announced that the captain wanted to see me on the bridge "in the uniform of the day." This summons made it clear that I was in trouble. After retrieving my cap I reported to the bridge where I was kept standing in trepidation for several minutes (perhaps only one or two), after which the captain turned ponderously and called me over to his stool where he was gazing over a glassy stretch of Atlantic ocean. With a few pauses and "ahems" he inquired about whether I had made preparations for dealing with the expectation of rampant venereal disease in Belgium. After my brief affirmation he said, "Very well. That will be all!" I got the message of silent admonition.

The trip took us to Antwerp and a chance to visit nearby Holland by trolley and foot. On crossing the border, we were struck by a sharp contrast in appearance of the geographically identical countryside. Although the Dutch had been shockingly devastated by the Wehrmacht, all the rubble was neatly stacked and swept and the landscape—marked with mine fields—was immaculate, whereas the Belgians had sold out and suffered no direct damage but the affect on their side of the line was dinghy, disheveled and dirty. That excursion to the little town of Bergen-op-Zoom, where we stopped at a sidewalk cafe for a beer, resulted in a memorable friendship. The café had no beer and we drank some nondescript beverage that they served instead. As we were leaving after paying our check two gentlemen approached us to report that we had been short-changed and to have the waiter rectify it. They turned out to be officers in the Dutch Navy who then graciously and generously took us to a house that was supposedly an officers club where we were treated to beer, schnapps, ham and cheese. These were precious hoardings which we were embarrassed to accept but they insisted that it was trivial gratitude for what we Americans had done to save their country. It was a delightful afternoon of conversation, war stories and speculations about the future. It was an encounter that made me proud to be an American and pleased to be appreciated. I corresponded with one of those officers for some years.

On another day during our stay in Antwerp, I ventured alone into Brussels. My meandering led me to a British officer's club, where I had a remarkable encounter. While having a drink at one end of a long bar, I heard surprisingly familiar songs emanating from the other end of the room. A group of British Navy medical officers were lustily singing songs from my HMS Aesculapian Club play, which I had helped to write and produce. Sidling into their sphere I joined in the song, which elicited a look of astonishment and a query about where I had learned it. I reversed the question before answering them and was told that the songs were from the Guy's (London) Hospital show of the previous year, which had obviously been purloined from our show. Naturally, they were skeptical about my assertion of authorship until I was able to recite several other songs from the play, which elicited respect and chagrin.

The second night of our quay side docking in Antwerp provided another encounter with our captain, to whom I was indebted for not throwing me into the brig for my hatless insolence. I had spent an exhausting evening administering to a large number of very obstreperous sailors returning from shore leave. It seems that almost the only available booze in town was a local brandy that must have contained some psychedelic ingredient because these men were not just drunk but were behaving in a highly unusual and boisterous manner. When the last sailor was sent to bed after an emetic at midnight I finally was able to turn in. An hour or so later, the captain's orderly appeared in my cabin to announce that the captain wanted to see me immediately. Grudgingly, I got dressed and reported to the captain's cabin. It turned out that he was furious about being awakened by Lieutenant Head, the assistant gunnery officer, who had come aboard on the officer's gangway just outside his cabin in a rowdy mood. I was instructed to go down and examine the culprit and "declare him drunk." That was a tough mission because the Navy considers "conduct unbecoming an officer and a gentleman" to be a serious offense that would be disastrously damaging to an officer's career—particularly to an Annapolis graduate. I proceeded to help the obviously intoxicated Mr. Head out of his clothes and into his bunk and returned to the waiting captain. I reported that Mr. Head appeared to have "had a drink or two on the beach, but I was unable to establish that he was intoxicated." The captain was furious at what he considered my insolence but he was unable to override a medical opinion. My luck with the captain held out once more and I was a hero to Mr. Head.

An historical footnote to that voyage was the announcement of the atom bombing of Hiroshima in the ship's newsletter. It heralded the surrender of Japan and the end of hostilities, which meant that our Pacific destination would be canceled. Consequently when we returned from Antwerp our ship was consigned to shuttling across the Atlantic to ferry troops home from LeHarve to New York. This allowed frequent reunions with Jane and the formulation of plans for our uncertain future.

Our ship had only a few minor encounters with German aircraft that were not able to inflict any significant damage but the most life-threatening experience of my time in the service occurred *after* the hostilities ended. We left LeHarve on December 19, 1945, on our second transport trip with our hangar deck filled with several hundred soldiers, bunked four deep. Our over-eager captain was determined to get the troops back for Christmas and maintained the ship's speed as we encountered a major North Atlantic storm. Force six winds led to waves of eighty feet or more that tossed this large ship about violently. Initially, few seemed concerned about the ship's integrity but we noted that our progress was marked with a violent shuddering crash after every third or fourth pitch as the bow emerged through a huge wave, hesitated and then dropped into the following trough to strike the water like a hammer. The dire consequence of this activity was predicted by the ship's damage control officer who pleaded with the captain to reduce speed. Of all the crew none were more salty with twenty plus years experience in every type of crisis. When *he,* of all people, became worried the word spread rapidly to trigger universal fear. Sure enough, a major crack appeared in the hull that threatened to break off the bow and sink the ship. We hove to for two days of valiant emergency damage control measures, wallowing crazily in a wild sea. Fortunately, the repairs held and the storm subsided enough to permit limping into New York harbor on Christmas afternoon. I arrived at the St John's apartment just in time to surprise Jane and her family as they sat down to dinner. It was a pleasant surprise for me to find my old room mate Hank Moorman, who had been an usher in our wedding, there as a welcome guest.

One of the pleasures of that period in the Navy was playing bridge virtually every evening in the ward room. Although the quality of our game was poor it was a stimulating experience and the initial impetus for an activity that has proven to be a feature of later life. This, of course, was only one aspect of the camaraderie among the officers in the Ward Room with whom I lived, played and worked during that period. I had a real taste of Navy life at its best and I enjoyed it—but not as a lifetime career.

When the war was over the *Philadelphia* was sent to be decommissioned in the Philadelphia Navy Yard and mothballed. All thoughts turned to getting out of the Navy and back to our careers, which was contingent on inventorying and closing out my medical department. Our captain promised that he would release me as soon as it was done. I left my bride in New York while I stayed on board and worked around the clock to complete the task in record time. True to his word, the captain sent my release to the bureau. My diligence, however, was rewarded by disappointing orders to another ship for the same dreary decommissioning process. Remembering my earlier luck at the Bureau of Medicine & Surgery, I petitioned the captain for permission to travel to Washington to plead my case. The captain, who could easily have exercised vengeance for my errant behavior by simply endorsing these unwelcome orders, kindly granted my request. My trip to Washington was successful in getting my orders to the other ship canceled and changed to the discharge center in Pleasanton, California, ending my active duty and freeing me to pursue my career.

My stint in the Navy, just short of two years, had been relatively easy and interesting. It was almost embarrassing to have fulfilled my patriotic duty with little discomfort and less disruption of my life than had had been the case for most of my contemporaries.

CHAPTER 9

Marriage

Perhaps the most indiscreet proclamation I ever made was a statement—expressed to my colleagues in medical school, was a triad of convictions about matrimony: 1) that I intended to marry a Western girl and not someone from the effete East, 2) that doctors should not marry nurses, and 3) that doctors' daughters should be avoided. My geographical prejudices were mellowed in the process of dating attractive ladies around Boston, several of whom would have been excellent spouses. But when the definitive step was finally taken I really had to eat crow. Oddly it was Libby Mills, a terrific girl in Boston whom I had been dating, who made the arrangements for me to meet one of her Vassar classmates who lived in New York. It was a blind date to which I objected vehemently and, as it turned out, so did the date.

Jane St. John was the eldest daughter of a prominent New York surgeon and of a distinguished nurse, who had received the Croix de Guerre and the Victoria Cross for her field hospital work in World War I. Jane had been educated in private girl's schools and graduated from Vassar in anticipation of going to medical school. She applied and was accepted at Columbia College of Physicians & Surgeons, but her father objected because she would "take the place of a man" in wartime and persuaded her to go to nursing school instead.

Jane and I met in New York at the apartment of my Uncle Dick Bertheau, who graciously hosted cocktails for us and two other HMS classmates, whose dates were nursing friends of Jane. I was smitten on first sight and the evening was gloriously enjoyable. Despite its brevity, the encounter totally convinced me that I had found the woman that I wanted to marry. There had been several bright, attractive ladies whom I had considered desirable but the circumstances of graduate school and no money dispelled any such thoughts. This was in the Spring of 1944 when I had a rare weekend off during the second year of surgical training at the MGH and it was certain that I would soon be going on active duty in the Navy. There was no conceivable possibility of pursuing a relationship. It was a crushing realization that this emergence of my dream girl, a rare combination of beauty, brains, and breeding, was to be just that, a memorable dream.

But my assignment to a ship that was just entering the Philadelphia Navy Yard for several months provided me with a reasonably proximate base from which to pursue a courtship. Of course, I had no reason to believe that I had a chance as a viable contender for such a prize, whom I assumed to have scores of more eligible suitors from both New York society and the professional world that surrounded her. It was, therefore, a pleasant surprise to have a positive response to my telephone inquiry and a thrilling pleasure to contemplate seeing her again. Jane—or "Sinjy" as she was called by her friends—was in her last year of nursing school at Columbia-Presbyterian Hospital and living in Maxwell Hall, the nursing dormitory. When I called for her in the lobby she seemed uncertain about recognizing me but some time later she confessed that it was an act to shield her delight. On every possible occasion, which amounted to no more than six or seven, I took the train to New York, picked up a gardenia corsage in Penn Station and enjoyed dinner and perhaps a nightclub with Jane. I proposed to her on the top of a 5th Avenue bus, but she delayed her reply until our next date. Christmas was spent with her family where I met her two sisters, who were equally beautiful with a strong resemblance. They were warmly accepting of this Western interloper and I felt very much at home with all of them. We announced our engagement on December 26, which initiated frenetic arrangements for a lovely wedding at St. James Church in New York, on January 20, less than eight months after our first date.

The wedding was notable for the many distinguished friends and relatives of the St. Johns and for a tiny handful of my relatives plus a few friends whose wartime travels happened to bring them to the area. An elegant reception at the Cosmopolitan Club put me on display to a critical New York crowd who received me with varying degrees of approval. An aunt of Jane's came down the receiving line, took my hand limply, silently inspected me from head to toe, and exclaimed, "Oh, but you're not going to take her way out *there* are you?"

After a brief skiing honeymoon at Mont Tremblant, in the Laurentian Mountains north of Montreal, we took up housekeeping for three months of relatively indolent social life in a small apartment in West Philadelphia with several other officers from the ship. It was glorious to have some time with my lovely new wife before sailing away to the Caribbean in the spring for a shakedown cruise. Jane returned to New York to live with her family and to resume her nursing at Presbyterian Hospital. She wrote loving and interesting letters to me every day, which I treasured. But I committed a terrible *faux pas* by disposing of them at the end of the war.

My discharge in California allowed Jane to look at the West for the first time and to recognize that many of my attitudes and objectives differed significantly from those of my family, largely as a consequence of my Boston experience and my professional outlook. Poignantly we became involved in a domestic dispute in which I had the opportunity to establish my loyalty to my bride by siding with her in a dispute over something my parents wanted her to do.

The time had come to focus attention on the completion of my surgical training. The importance of board certification had been amplified by the war service and the armed services' policy of preferential ranking and assignments of doctors who were certified. Naturally, my first choice was to return to the MGH but my inquiry revealed that there was no room for all five classes of residents whose training had been interrupted by the war, so I began searching for other training programs where I could fulfill this goal. That quest was also discouraging because other programs had the same challenge of fitting multiple classes of returnees into their current resident staffs. It was, therefore, a great relief to receive a letter from Dr. Churchill inviting me back to the MGH to complete my training. Of my sixteen classmates who started as interns only two of us got the nod to join the trainees already present along with those selected from the other four returning classes. The resulting group consisted of high performers and seasoned veterans, which should have given me cause to reflect on *how* fortunate I was to be among them.

The consequence of this coveted appointment, however, was to move back to Boston to live in a semi-tenement on the back side of Beacon Hill and to resume the rigorous schedule of a surgical resident. It was a tough assignment for a new bride, and particularly for a girl who had always enjoyed luxurious living and had no experience with deprivation. But the medical background of her parents and their hardship experience together during World War I was supportive and Jane adapted with commendable good cheer. She got a job as a research technician in the Bacteriology Department at the Harvard Medical School and we made the most of a frugal existence out of my salary of $46/mo, her salary of $90/mo, and the GI Bill that paid $90/mo, plus an occasional under the counter infusion from her family. We were poor but thankfully did not have to incur any debt, which is the scourge of today's medical graduates who face repaying up to $100,000 in student loans. Despite our financial restrictions, Jane maintained a welcome home-site and never complained. We were very much in love and looked forward to a bright future after completing my training. This was a happy and satisfying period thanks to the friendships, the institutional identity and the Boston ambiance. As we residents worked up the ladder and learned from many demanding surgeons our competence grew rapidly in an atmosphere of give-and-take, which we later learned to be exceptional. It was a blossoming era of surgical training, during which residents were allowed considerable freedom and responsibility under acutely critical oversight. Jane and I decided it was time to start our family, despite our meager resources and tenement circumstances. At first, I was reluctant to take this step that would constrain our freedom but Jane persuaded me away from my position.

My good fortune was not only at the expense of Jane's potential as a physician that was aborted by her father, but also as a person with exceptional intellect, people skills, and organizational ability that could have challenged the talents of many a high level executive. I realize that our marriage would probably never have occurred if she had pursued her capabilities. Her enormous benefits to my life came at a price of my coping with a bright, strong-minded, and determined woman, whose background provoked her to fulfill all of the traditional responsibilities of a wife and mother, but who was not to be subservient to or manipulated by her husband. It is a constant challenge to keep up with her.

The saga of our fifty-six year marriage and the raising of two wonderful children is intertwined with all the subsequent events in this chronicle. Without Jane much of it would have been impossible.

CHAPTER 10

Sojourn With Science

A nother chapter in my life that proved to be of cardinal importance was an unpredicted interruption of my surgical training to be sent away from the hospital for a year, which at the time seemed to be an impediment to my objective. The log-jam of post-war returning veterans in the residency program prevented the orderly progress of seniority and succession to the coveted chief residency year on one of the two surgical services. The format of assignments was extremely variable to accommodate the training requirements for board certification of a group whose experience, both in prior training and in war service had been diverse. Some could get credit for their time in the military, thus reducing their needs for board approval, and others were anxious to get started in practice and disinclined to prolong their training in order to get the top job. Surgical trainees at MGH obtained significant operative experience during the assistant residency, unlike some programs in which all the operating was done by the chief resident. Juggling the available rotations to meet the needs of such a heterogeneous group was a challenge that necessitated some innovative planning. Conveniently and perhaps coincidentally the leadership group began to anticipate that science and scientific methodology would play an important role in the future of academic surgery. This combination of factors provoked my chief and mentor, Dr. Churchill, to initiate a custom, later a requirement, for those participants in the surgical residency who expected to complete the full program to take a year or more out of clinical training for some experience in basic science research. I was one of the first trainees to be offered that opportunity as a stepping stone to the chief residency. A role in academia was an aspect of my future that had never entered my mind and I shared the typical post war attitude that we needed to get on with our careers. However the influence of my mentor was powerful and I was easily talked into applying for and being awarded a National Research Fellowship to spend a year in the Physiology Department at HMS, working under the guidance of that department's famous chairman, Eugene Landis, one of the country's leading physiologists. As was later to prove fortuitous, my assignment in that department was to work with my classmate, Cliff Barger, on a project involving cardiac function. Cliff, as one of the brightest members of our class, was a stimulating and energetic person to work with in the early stage of his career that was destined to achieve world renown as a cardiovascular physiologist and subsequently as the department chairman to succeed Landis.

That sojourn away from the clinical pathway proved to be an exceedingly valuable and most interesting aspect of my life. It had several virtues: 1) It taught me the intellectual discipline of critical scientific research and the knowledge for sophisticated evaluation of scientific and clinical reports that I would be reading for the rest of my life, 2) It provided an opportunity to reflect on the world of clinical surgery from the remote critical perspective of pure academia, 3) It expanded my surgical capabilities with the chance to develop and create animal models for scientific studies on my own, 4) It presented an open-ended indulgence of my bent for mechanical innovation, 5) Perhaps most importantly—it gave me the equivalent of an intensive post graduate course in physiology which later was of great advantage in the development of cardiac surgery. Of course, the latter was a concept whose time had not yet come, but its emergence was fostered by this kind of background superimposed on surgical chutzpah and technical innovation.

The important experimental project in which I participated was one of the first studies of heart function during exercise and stress. All prior information about cardiac dynamics had been obtained in the resting state, both clinically and experimentally. Our protocol was to measure the previously undocumented parameters of cardiac function in normal, healthy hearts during strenuous exercise as contrasted to cardiac performance at rest. Later these measurements were contrasted with those in hearts whose performance had been impaired with surgically damaged valves or obstructed flow that simulated the common causes of heart failure. The data was obtained from cardiac catheters—positioned in the hearts of dogs—to obtain data while they were running on a treadmill.

That experimental model necessitated two unprecedented feats: first we had to train dogs to run on the treadmill inside a cage, which turned out to be relatively easy and something they seemed to enjoy doing once they learned how. Then we had to persuade them to undergo introduction of the catheter through a trocar (sharp pointed tube) into the jugular vein in the neck while they were awake under local anesthesia on a fluoroscopy table in a dark room. We were amazed how easily we found several dogs who trusted us so completely that they remained docile for this routine. Indeed, some of them, when led into the fluoroscopy room, would voluntarily jump up onto the table where they would lie quietly in the dark, without restraints, to accept their neck puncture. And then, when led onto the treadmill, they were eager to get going. Undoubtedly some animal rights activists would be indignant about that process, but we actually had a mutual friendship with these dogs who provided us with information of great importance and really seemed to enjoy it. Critics would have been surprised to see how trusting and affectionate the dogs were with us "tormentors," how amenable they were to our procedures, and how patient they were as we made our measurements. Dogs are very expressive and I never saw one of them struggle or look frightened or cowed. It appeared that our work was their recreation. Of course, some were more cooperative and suitable than others, so we selected the better ones. But I can guarantee that none were the subjects of torture or intimidation.

Not only did they teach us some valuable physiology but we also learned about their remarkable traits. For example, they were housed in cages with wire mesh flooring over a funneled bottom which was designed to gather their urine for analysis. But the apparatus failed its objective because the dogs would almost never urinate in the cage—even if left for more than twenty-four hours. We had to resort to walking them outside with one of us following along to catch the urine in a large beaker under a lifted leg. Needless to say this little daily scenario provided great amusement to onlookers. Regrettably, we were less successful in dealing with their defecation. Walking them around the parking lot on a leash was insufficient stimulus to empty their bowels but within a minute or two of running on the treadmill they would let go and we never could stop the tread in time to catch the feces before it ran around into the machinery. As a consequence this laboratory with all its sophisticated instrumentation was stinky. It proved that we can become accustomed to almost anything.

These experiments provided some of the first information about the significant differences between cardiac function during exercise and at rest to reflect on the misinformation that had pervaded the literature about accelerated hearts. In the process of expanding the scope of our study to include cardiac function under stress it was necessary to devise operations on these dogs to create artificial obstructions. This exercise led to discovering a significant fact that applies to all conduits. That is, if a tube is progressively narrowed or obstructed the flow through it will not be impaired in proportion to the degree of obstruction as might be expected, but remains essentially unchanged until a critical degree of narrowing is reached (somewhere between 80% and 90%) at which point the resistance rises precipitously. This phenomenon has important implications in numerous clinical conditions.

Scientific discovery as the result of tedious and laborious experimental procedure is most gratifying, if not spectacular. It was both stimulating and enlightening to share thought processes with the members of a distinguished basic science department, certainly a sharp contrast to the frenetic and exhausting world of clinical surgery. The luncheon chatter of great minds of a different sort was exciting. Their seminars, at which we presented various phases of our work, were exceedingly analytical. The discipline of pure science precludes any speculation and conclusions must be limited to what can be mathematically proven with statistical significance.

This fellowship year in the Department of Physiology was, however, not entirely a one-way street. The surgical perspective and personality was also useful to the scientist. Problem solving, innovation, and technical capability in creating the animal models were all useful skills that I was able to contribute in partial exchange for all that I learned from the scientists.

The wisdom and foresight of Dr. Churchill in sending me away from and postponing my hospital training (which I would never have elected to do) is attested by the recognition of its great benefits. In addition to what I learned about cardiac physiology and the critical analysis of professional research, I was also privileged to indulge my bent for tinkering with and developing gadgetry in the department's well equipped workshop. Among other things I built a sigmoidoscope out of Lucite tubing with a light source at the outer end to transmit a bright light along the tube. It was a useful instrument that was never patented or produced—just a toy that was fun to make.

This was a period of relative leisure that provided the time to be with my family and the time to travel. The schedule of a researcher is relatively low-key, which gave Jane and me a chance to enjoy Boston's charms and virtues. Not a small feature of this impecunious period was the occasional visit by Jane's mother who would arrive from New York with two pieces of baggage: one a tiny valise with her personal things, and the other a large valise containing two huge steaks and two bottles of whiskey. Our first child was born just before beginning that fellowship and we left him with Jane's mother at the age of three months while we took off on an exploratory excursion across country by car. This trip served the double purpose of allowing Jane to emerge from her Gotham provinciality by showing her something of the vast country and of allowing us to examine some of the possibilities for future practice. Our frugal resources made it prudent to plan the trip so as to see and stay with friends along the way.

One of our first stops was in Cleveland at the home of Jim Shannon, who had recently completed his neurosurgical residency at the MGH. We spent the warm summer afternoon in his back yard drinking mint juleps (I think four of us went through two fifths of bourbon). There was considerable revelry, the upshot of which was to target our most infamous prankster, Henry Moorman. Hank was then doing a stint at the Snyder Clinic in Winfield, Kansas, where we phoned him collect and each of us indulged in endless chatter. A short time later Hank tried to retaliate by reversing the process but Shannon mustered enough aplomb through his alcoholic haze to refuse the charge and to convince the operator that the caller was one of his dangerously demented patients who should be apprehended by the police. We later learned that Hank did get a brief visit from the men in blue.

The next stop on that trip was at the Mayo Clinic in Rochester, Minnesota, where we stayed with one of Jane's nursing school classmates and I was shown around by Dr. Howard Gray, one of Dr. St. John's surgical colleagues. It was an impressive experience that I have always remembered because it demonstrated the unique skills of practicing medicine with great efficiency without sacrificing compassion and personal attention. It has never ceased to amaze me that this highly visible, world-renowned institution had mastered these skills long before 1940, whereas the profession at large eschewed the opportunity for half a century only to have it forcibly imposed on them in the form of managed care in the '90s. The smoothly running, comfortable productivity of the Mayo Clinic is impressive and could have been the model for a national medical practice that would have obviated the mess that it has become at the close of the century. As a surgeon who has operated in community hospitals, a county hospital, a university hospital and a veterans hospital the efficiency of my time probably never exceeded 20% (in terms of utilizing my skills as distinct from what others can do). In Rochester, that efficiency is increased to better than 80% simply by better organization, utilizing secondary personnel to handle details. Surgeons almost never waste any time prepping, draping, making and closing incisions, etc., let alone having to wait between cases. Without any greater technical speed the average Mayo surgeon can perform four or five operations per day in the same time and effort it would take me to do one or two, not because they worked more rapidly but just because their work was so effectively facilitated.

Among the measures not seen elsewhere that impressed me in 1947 and subsequently were in the clockwork precision of operating room procedure. Surgeons operated only three days a week and each had two or more operating rooms between which he rotated without having to wait for his first case to be finished and closed by his assistants and the room prepared for the next case. His second case was started in the alternate room while he was doing the first, so that when he scrubbed in the procedure had reached a stage that could utilize his expertise immediately. There was hardly time between cases to empty his bladder or to grab more than one bite of a sandwich. Every measure possible was utilized to save the surgeon's time and energy, thus easing his work process and allowing him to accomplish more. For example, the anesthetist was alert to the operative routine and would push a button a moment before he anticipated the surgeon would leave the room. As a consequence, there were *two* stenographers standing in the hallway to take dictation of the operative report while the surgeon walked about seventy-five feet to the dressing room. When the surgeons made their rounds to see patients in their rooms, all new x-rays and laboratory studies were displayed for instant viewing and if the patient's incision needed examining the dressing would be removed ahead of time, all of which permitted a thorough and effective visit in a matter of one or two minutes. This may sound like working on a factory production line but from my viewpoint the extra productivity extracted from the surgeon was far more desirable than the alternative of impatient waiting and frustrating delay.

From Rochester, we drove west through the Dakota Badlands, the Rocky Mountains of Montana, and the wheat fields of eastern Washington state to the lovely city of Seattle where I made some calls, visited the University of Washington hospitals, and got some encouragement from Dr. John Schilling, an HMS colleague, a few years my senior.

We then drove to San Francisco and examined the local prospects. Although there was no evidence of eager anticipation for my presence on the professional scene I was received cordially both at Stanford by Dr. Emile Holman, and at U.C. by Dr. H. Glenn Bell, probably on the strength of my training background but it was undoubtedly also helpful to have Dr. F. B. St. John as a father-in-law and to have known Dr. Howard Naffziger, the former Chief of Surgery, as a child through my father. Since San Franciso was my home it was comforting to recognize the possibility of practicing there but no one offered any invitation. Happily for me, Jane liked the City and the people she met so it remained a viable option.

Then on to Denver, where we were cordially shown around by Hugh McMillan, a HMS and MGH surgeon who was a couple of years older than me. Here the circumstances were attractive and practice opportunities more definitive.

All in all, it was an interesting and productive trip that introduced Jane to a large segment of the country and me to a first-hand view of surgical practices outside of Boston. It was too soon to make any decision about an ultimate destination and we had not yet closed the idea of staying in the Boston area, which had been more or less home for ten years. It was the beginning of realizing that a lifetime attachment to institutional apron strings needed to be severed.

Back in the saddle at the Physiology Department I became absorbed in the technical and intellectual challenges of our project. In collaboration with Charles Hufnagle I developed an operation to narrow the pulmonary artery to a precisely critical degree that would increase the pressure and the work of the right ventricle (which pumps blood into the pulmonary artery) enough to allow us to study the functional consequences but just short of a degree that would be fatal. We found that exquisite definition to be very difficult to achieve[vi].

During this period, I participated in department seminars for which I had to present dissertations on various concepts and on our experimental results. These exercises, under the scrutiny of the department's professional scientists, were of great value for my then unanticipated academic future. It was gratifying to be a participant in several publications that emanated from that year of comparative leisure[vii].

In the six month interval between the completion of the fellowship and the beginning of my chief residency I had the fortuitous opportunity to be hired as the interim (paid, but not much) assistant to Richard Sweet, the then famous thoracic surgeon at the MGH who pioneered esophageal resection and early cardiac procedures. He was a superb technician and a charming gentleman from whom I learned many gems of technique and management during my brief but memorable apprenticeship.

An unanticipated sequel to this sojourn into science was my affiliation with the Cardiovascular Research Institute (CVRI) at USCF. Shortly after my return to San Francisco and becoming involved with cardiovascular research I was appointed to the Cardiovascular Research Committee, which was charged with planning how the unfinished space on the thirteenth floor of the newly built Moffitt Hospital was to be utilized. The committee's role included the selection of a director for this new enterprise and—true to local tradition—those initially under consideration were in-house candidates. To the committee's credit they did accede to my persuasion to broaden their search across the country. In that quest someone suggested that the person who would be most qualified to provide the names of potential candidates would be Julius Comroe, a distinguished physician and research scientist in Philadelphia. When he was asked for recommendations his response was, "How about me?" His recruitment proved to be a seminal event for the whole campus. Thus began a fledging Institute that thrived under his wise and experienced guidance. In a remarkably short space of time Julius raised money, got facilities constructed, recruited bright young scientists, and began producing outstanding research. This new enterprise achieved world-wide recognition even before it was dry behind the ears that far surpassed anything else on the campus. The "tail was wagging the dog" and the direction of campus politics became an issue between two titans: the colorful superego of Chancellor John B. deC.M Saunders, and the skillful manipulation of the new Institute director. During the next few years, provoked by Comroe, the faculty underwent a complete metamorphosis with chairmen for the first time being recruited from all over the country, and the school achieving a level of excellence that began to rival even Harvard.

It was a privilege to be the only surgical member of the institute staff and my research benefited significantly from participating in its proceedings and seminars. But most valued was my association with one of the greatest men in my experience. Julius was a marvel at inspiring and guiding those around him with consummate skill. He instituted weekly seminars at which on-going research was discussed and criticized. Every paper to be presented at a scientific meeting was videotaped for the author's review after a trial run to the Institute staff. He held weekly executive sessions with his senior staff to discuss administrative problems and projects, carefully considering all opinions and seeking a consensus. But he made all the decisions solo. Everyone respected his methods because we knew that our thoughts were heard and we had complete confidence in his judgment, even when it differed from our individual opinion. Comroe has to be one of the leading figures of the century in medical science. I treasure having had his friendship and the benefit of his wisdom. Of my many affiliations, none has been more satisfying than being a member of the famous CVRI.

CHAPTER 11

The Pinnacle of a Chief Residency

The miracle of surviving the competition of getting into Harvard, of attaining upper echelon status within that select group, of attaining the coveted internship at the MGH, and of being half of a lucky pair from my class who came back after the war was far beyond what I had reason to expect. I had only wanted to get sufficient training to qualify for certification by the American Board of Surgery. I would have been proud and more than satisfied with fulfilling that requirement, which the MGH appeared to be providing to all those who were taken back on the resident staff after the war. To be selected for the coveted apex of the residency pyramid for the extra year as the chief resident on the East Surgical Service was the pinnacle of my career. I am embarrassed to recall that it all just seemed to happen so naturally that I never stopped to appreciate how fortunate I was or how many worthy contemporaries had been left behind.

This appointment was the crown jewel of surgical training at the time. It was the dawn of modern specialization in which lengthy, structured training programs were the prelude to examination and certification by a specialty Board. Prior to World War II, these boards were in various stages of development with spotty recognition and had relatively little impact on surgical practice. Doctors who chose to operate could do so with few constraints, except in teaching hospitals, and these surgeon's qualifications varied widely. There were few other surgical residencies of more than a couple of years and operative experience had to be attained by lengthy apprenticeship or just by observing. For an aspiring surgeon to acquire any substantial degree of skill took many years, lots of luck, and almost certainly a substantial amount of inept fumbling before becoming adept.

A chief residency in a first class teaching hospital was a quantum leap over a whole generation of physicians. At the age of thirty-two, I was put in charge of a service doing over a thousand cases a year. I could choose which cases to operate on myself, which ones to delegate to my assistant residents, and which ones to guide others through. It was an ideal experience that combined opportunity and autonomy with strong institutional oversight by attending surgeons and a chief of service who saw to it that our performance was as close to flawless as possible. It was a heady experience, exciting, gratifying, challenging and a tremendous pleasure.

The learning process was intense as we encountered a wide variety of problems and situations. Faculty mentors were always available for advice and guidance, but my technical abilities at that stage were well enough developed that it was almost never necessary to be displaced as surgeon. But help was welcomed when I got in over my head. I have vivid memories of facing dilemmas that caused me to sweat pretty hard: bleeding that seemed impossible to control, anatomic landmarks that weren't where they were supposed to be, tissue that would not hold sutures, septic pockets that could not be found. Every episode expanded my knowledge and capability, and years later these lessons would have their value emphasized when similar situations were encountered in practice.

As chief resident I was accountable only to the chief of service whose weekly inspections and case reviews were described above. All the assignments and activities I had delegated to my subordinate house officers were my responsibility to account for. If they goofed it was my fault. Criticism kept me on my toes, reminding me that it was *his* service even though I was running it. There was no whitewashing. The apparent basis for every death was privately graded in the chief's "little black book" as E.D.(error in diagnosis), E.T.(error in technique), E.M.(error in management), E.J. (error in judgment) or P.D. (patient's disease). There was nothing vindictive or punitive in the discussion and the errors were not meant to reflect negligence or irresponsibility but rather the perspective of hindsight and the quest for perfection. These meetings were tough but immensely valuable from a teaching standpoint. I believe they were the most important aspect of the training program.

Probably the most memorable of those meetings was the occasion when I was admonished not for some clinical shortcoming but for the inferred failure of the resident staff to perform up to its superlative expectations. On that afternoon it was evident that our chief, Dr. Allen, was so piqued and distracted that he virtually ignored the M&M reports. He revealed his dismay to be in that day's announcement of next year's surgical intern selections. For the first time in a dozen or more years, one of the applicants that had been on the MGH's first choice list had turned us down in favor of Johns Hopkins, which resulted in taking our seventh choice to get six recruits. This was looked on as a disgrace. Dr. Allen's attitude did not suggest that we belonged to an exclusive club but rather that our reputation had been threatened and remedy was in order. This occurrence was considered to be a reflection on our teaching popularity, for which the house staff could be held accountable as those in closest contact with the medical students. We were thus reminded of our responsibility for the prestige of the hospital among students.

A significant sidelight to this final year was the recent introduction of penicillin into civilian practice (Its limited supply had been reserved for the military during the war.) It was considered to be a "miracle drug" that would obliterate the dreaded septic complications of surgery. And because the drug was thought to be non-toxic it was a prevalent opinion that it should be given to every surgical patient to prevent infection from occurring. It occurred to me, however, that this might have long term detrimental consequences, so we conferred with Boston's leading bacteriologists, Chester Keefer and Max Finland, who agreed with a more restrictive use of the antibiotic. An informal protocol was set up with Bill McDermott, my counterpart as chief resident on the West Surgical Service, to compare the results of different antibiotic policies on the two services that derived patients from a common pool and functioned in the same facilities. My service would use no penicillin prophylactically and give it only for active infection or known contamination, and would limit its use to five days. Whereas on Bill's service every patient would get penicillin on a preventive basis and it would be used liberally for infections. At the end of six months we had each done about 700 cases and the data showed no benefit from prophylaxis. Indeed the infection rate on my service was slightly *lower* than his (but not statistically significant). That finding convinced Bill to abandon his routine and history has subsequently proven the value of that position. Regrettably, we were both too busy to recognize the historical significance of that little clinical experiment and to document the data for publication. It is fascinating to speculate what impact it might have had to abort the massive misuse of antibiotics, which now—fifty years later—is recognized as a serious threat. Our civilization is now plagued with massive invasion by bacteria that have developed resistance to most—or even all—antibiotics and threaten to bring back infection as a major killer.

It might be said that we were prophets of doomsday and perhaps our efforts to restrain the use of antibiotics were not strong enough. I have preached and written about using antibiotics only for identified bacterial infections but physicians were seduced by the superficial logic of preventing or aborting septic episodes and were frightened by the potential accusation of negligence if they *did not* give these miracle drugs for even the slightest indication. It is notable that this grave threat has appeared in recent novels and on television documentaries and is widely recognized as a parallel to the progressive failure of pesticides. Yet most physicians continue to give antibiotics indiscriminately at the risk of a world-wide plague of incurable infection.

Interesting experiences were frequent during this frenetic training period but some were more dramatic than others. One day, I was standing in the cafeteria line with Dr. Fiorendo Simeone describing a patient that I had just admitted with a tetanus infection. He asked if I had done a tracheostomy (airway tube in the neck) because the muscle spasm characteristic of this disease is prone to affecting the larynx and shutting off the airway. Just as I was reassuring him that the patient was stable and well sedated in a dark and quiet room to prevent any triggering stimulus, the paging microphones announced an emergency call for me. Ordinarily I would have found a telephone to inquire about the problem but with Sime's admonition hardly past my eardrums I dashed directly to the elevator and arrived to find my tetanus patient in acute spasm of his larynx, unable to breathe and getting blue. I was just in time to do a life-saving emergency tracheostomy at his bedside. It was a lesson I would not forget and a coincidence to substantiate my belief that I learned more surgery in the doctor's dining room and at M&M conferences than I did in the operating room.

The essence of this important year was, nevertheless, doing surgery, and lots of it, in the process of which our technical skills improved, our experience with unusual circumstances expanded, our ability to teach and utilize assistants improved, and our knowledge of the disease processes grew. Because we generally operated without attending surgeon guidance, there were occasions that relied upon developing ingenuity, but help was always available when needed.

Ordeals were the essence of a chief residency. There was little pedantic about our learning experience and lots of psychological trauma associated with our charge. It was not for the tender-hearted. At weekly grand rounds, where we presented patients to the senior staff, our role could be likened to that of Roman gladiators subject to heckling and critical second guessing. Straightforward cases, even if some aspect was remarkable, were usually passed off with little comment, and almost invariably the lively commentary was about controversial issues and what someone considered to be inappropriate about our management. Occasionally, we were able to retaliate by setting up situations that would predictably elicit critical comments, for which we had withheld a trump card to embarrass the critic. It was a fascinating game of David and Goliath to which people came from far and near, not just to see interesting cases but also for the contretemps in dialogue between teacher and pupil. Little did we appreciate the rarity and privilege of such open discussion and such depth of expertise. There was no room for authoritarianism or persiflage; indeed the discussions frequently generated strong outspoken disagreements among the faculty. Sitting in the front row at these sessions were illustrious names such as Leland McKittrick, Robert Linton, Reginald Smithwick, Oliver Cope, Marshall Bartlett, Joe Meigs, Henry Marble as well as the two service chiefs, Arthur Allen and Pete Churchill. Close behind them were mentors-to-be such as Claude Welch, Gordon Scannell, Lamar Soutter, "Butch" Donaldson, and a host of surgeons from the community. Francis Moore was among the young bucks on the staff until he was appointed to be chief at the Peter Bent Brigham Hospital, one of Harvard's other teaching hospitals next to the medical school.

The unique aspect of Harvard's clinical teaching program was the keen intramural competition between the several affiliated hospitals for students and resident staffs. Unlike every other medical school, Harvard owns and runs no hospital with its name but instead has arranged with several Boston hospitals to appoint and control their clinical staffs with members of their faculty. Thus Franny Moore's appointment (at the unprecedented age of only thirty-two) to a prestigious chair was within the Harvard family.

Critiques of the resident staff were purely in the spirit of learning by analysis, and if they seemed vindictive or shameful it was due to high expectations. This, we rapidly learned, was to be accepted like the rough and tumble of football. It did hurt our feelings at first, never to hear a word of praise when we thought we had achieved a triumph, but eventually I got the silent message that "You wouldn't be here if you weren't *expected* to be good and a compliment about your performance implies that it wasn't expected." How is that for elitism?

It is impossible to do justice to this seminal year in these few pages but virtually every moment of the experience is indelible for its great opportunity, exciting challenge, encyclopedic learning, and great fun. I wear the badge of the MGH with pride and gratitude along with the other products of this program, who continue to provide leadership generation after generation.

CHAPTER 12

The Moseley Fellowship

Another important chapter in my life emerged from a backhanded sequence of events. Having delayed my career with two years in the Navy and then extended my post graduate training by almost two additional years, first with the Fellowship in Physiology at the medical school, followed by an extra six months on stand-by, working as an assistant to Dr. Sweet before starting my chief residency, I felt that I was reaching a saturation point. I was seven and a half years out of medical school with a wife and two small children, and no money. Provoked by an urge to settle down at long last, I went to see my chief, Dr. Churchill, after nine months of my twelve-month residency appointment, for permission to finish a little early to get started with making a living. The unexpected result of this request was his concession that I had enough training and some discussion about whether I would like to stay on in Boston. When I told him of my determination to return to San Francisco he strongly recommended that I obtain some perspective about Boston before moving to a new venue. He proposed to nominate me for Harvard's prestigious Moseley Traveling Fellowship, which was endowed by the family of an MGH intern who had died climbing the Matterhorn, which was awarded each year to one HMS graduate at the completion of his surgical residency training, for an open-ended sojourn abroad, which Dr. Churchill had himself once enjoyed. This was an honor and opportunity that was impossible to refuse, despite not being my objective and a further postponement of settling down. Both Jane's and my parents were opposed to this unnecessary prolongation of our financially deprived state and contended that enough was enough. But I could not muster the courage to turn down the fellowship even though it would have been the sensible thing to do.

Churchill graciously arranged for me to start my tour with his old friend and colleague, Sir James Learmonth at the Royal Infirmary of Edinburgh, Europe's leading light in the new and burgeoning field of vascular surgery. The fellowship stipend was $3600 for the year, just enough to get there and live on with a little support from our families.

We moved our skimpy belongings out of our Beacon Hill basement apartment to the St. John house in Woodstock, Vermont, and took off by train in early November for Quebec to catch a ship to Scotland. Our baggage included cases of canned baby food for two-year-old David and eight-month-old Virginia because of the reported food shortages in the U.K. By any sensible evaluation it was idiotic to undertake moving the family to the cold, dark, austerity of a post-war Scottish winter, but fortunately we were young, flexible, and enthusiastic, and it turned out to be one of the most memorable and enjoyable chapters in our lives. Never before or since have we encountered such cordial reception and generous hospitality from strangers. Perhaps the Harvard/MGH trappings were a factor but they do not explain how so many of these Edinburghians became our lifetime friends.

After a somewhat stormy North Atlantic crossing from Quebec we arrived in Edinburgh to begin our stay in a residential hotel where our room was minimally warmed by a small coin operated electric heater that consumed a shilling every twenty minutes. We soon learned to tolerate the cold. Later, we moved to a four room flat in a small cul-de-sac near the zoo, where we took up housekeeping and shared the rigors of a devastated post-war economy. Houses had no central heating and were poorly insulated with their only heat coming from small, inefficient fireplaces. Our coal ration was three sacks a month, hardly sufficient to maintain a small hearth fire in the dining room where we lived and where the peak afternoon temperature got up to about 60° F, while the rest of the flat was necessarily at outdoor temperature. Getting into bed between cold and clammy sheets was torture until we learned about the "porcelain pig", a large ceramic bottle that got filled with boiling water and swept around in the bed before retiring. Edinburgh's winters are seldom freezing but are constantly damp and gloomy. Tons of coal smoke rendered the fog to be more dense than I had ever encountered in San Francisco. Once I descended from a tram in mid morning and was unable to see the curb less than fifteen feet away.

It is fortunate that we did not find it too difficult to deal with discomfort and deprivation (The week's meat ration would fit on a serving spoon and we got only two eggs a week) but there was real culture shock associated with both the social and professional experience. The Scots were all cordial but very reserved until they had cautiously decided that you were OK, then they became friends for life. They were tolerant of their American allies but expected them to be a little uncivilized so we provided a pleasant surprise. Of course we had the advantage of being sponsored by Professor Learmonth, who had spent three years at the Mayo Clinic and had an American wife, having married Will Mayo's secretary. He had a reputation of being grumpy and demanding to his staff but to me he was like an indulging uncle. I frequently sat and read in his office, which provided the rare opportunity for many interesting informal conversations. On ward rounds he would alternately chide me or commend me for my pronunciation of medical terms or my recitation of some surgical axiom.

When I innocently signed up to take the examination for fellowship in the Royal College of Surgeons, thinking it would be a cinch after recently passing my American Board of Surgery exams, Learmonth adroitly deflected me by suggesting that it would be a more educational to sit with the examining team. It became evident that he had graciously spared me the embarrassment of failure because the British have far more intense teaching in anatomy and I certainly would certainly have flunked that part of the examination. And it turned out that this experience on the giving end of examining would be of value a few years later when I began to examine for the American Board of Thoracic Surgery.

Scrubbing with his surgical team was a most interesting revelation of a different system of surgical training as well as a different operating procedure. Whereas during my chief residency I had done essentially *all* the surgery on the ward service, almost none of the surgery at the Royal Infirmary was done by anyone other than the professor himself. Even the senior attending surgeons in their fifties would do only the occasional case in the professor's absence and the registrars (counterparts of U.S. residents) were allowed only to observe and hold retractors but actually did no major surgery whatsoever. From a technical perspective surgical assistants in the U.S. were almost always active participants in the procedure, sharing major portions of the technical steps. But Sir James used his assistants only to hold retractors while he held two or three instruments at once, doing all the suturing, tying, and cutting himself. Sterile technique was far from strict and wound reconstruction was far less meticulous than the layer by layer technique I had been taught. Yet the patients did surprisingly well and had few complications. These contrasts were a revelation to one who had been indoctrinated in the "right way" to do things and who believed that otherwise was disastrous.

The most auspicious event of my Edinburgh sojourn began with what appeared to be a rather casual request by a pair of medical students to come and speak, to what I interpreted to be a club, about surgical training in the U.S. I gladly assented to their invitation with the expectation of an informal bull session over a beer or two and gave it little thought. When the professor heard about it and asked if I had brought my black tie for the occasion I realized that something else was in the offing. Then to my surprise, placards appeared on the hospital bulletin boards announcing a lecture at the Royal Medical Society with my name boldly emblazoned as the speaker representing the Massachusetts General Hospital. Suddenly I realized that this was not a casual matter and that I needed to prepare an appropriate speech.

When the appointed evening arrived, I found myself on the dais of a small, stately, book-lined auditorium, sitting between the president, Mr. Tommy Miller, enthroned above me on my right and an elaborate encasement containing an illuminated document on my left. As the proceedings got around to my introduction, the president compounded my anxiety by informing me that this was the oldest English-speaking medical society in the world and that I was their first American speaker in over a hundred years. He added an informational note that the display on my left was the society's charter, which was signed by King George III, about whom my impressions were probably unfriendly. All of these unexpected trappings, added to the formally attired audience of distinguished faculty and students, made my approach to the speaker's rostrum a bit tremulous. Of course I was highly flattered and properly impressed with my responsibility but nonetheless undaunted in my naïve determination to tell them the merits and the mechanics of mid-twentieth century American surgery, which had surpassed its European heritage. I think I succeeded in at least not offending the professors whose dynasties and prerogatives were challenged by my suggestions, but I know that the students and younger staff were intrigued by a system that seemed to them an impossible utopia at that time. It was a stimulating evening and I enjoyed the possibility that it just may have been the foretelling of Europe's subsequent emulation of American training and practice standards.

I cannot do justice to the hospitality we enjoyed during that brief sojourn, particularly because their restricted post-war resources and the miserable winter weather were hardly conducive to entertaining, and also because we were just young visitors that really did not warrant troubling over. We were invited to dinner by members of the faculty whom we did not know but who felt indebted for hospitality they had received in America. We were invited to a series of Scottish country dances, to a fancy University Club Ball and to trips in the countryside. Our neighbors in our little cul-de-sac of seven houses, called *St. John's Garden,* were politely distant until New Year's Eve (their *Hogmanaigh,* which supersedes Christmas). As we returned from a dinner elsewhere and switched on a light the phone rang and a voice asked, "Be ye home?" It was a neighbor inviting us to his house where we met all the residents of the cul-de-sac who were celebrating what we would call a block party. Thereafter we were on cordial terms with all of them and even recipients of an occasional pair of farm eggs for "the wee pet," our little daughter, whom they adored.

We developed what would become lasting friendships with several members of the staff as well as Sir James and his charming wife Charlotte. Donald and Diana Douglas (he later to become chairman of surgery in Dundee, to be knighted and be the Queen's surgeon) were exceptionally cordial to us and introduced us to their lay friends. Among the latter was Lancelot Cormack and his wife Gertrude. He was a publisher who kindly volunteered to make a bookplate for me, which I have used all my life. It is a Vesalius print of a skeleton standing against a dais on which the second aphorism of Aristotle has been added; the latter is chiseled on a marble wall of the Harvard Medical School. (See frontispiece).

Sadly, this interesting and enjoyable adventure was aborted before we could complete the planned travel to other centers of surgery around the UK and on the continent. Early in my residency, I had been examining a tuberculosis patient with an open tube bronchoscope and he accidentally coughed some sputum into my eye. Despite the immediate precautions of irrigation and Argyrol drops in my eye, my tuberculin skin test turned positive a few months later to verify that I had become infected. Chest x-rays were negative but I was admonished to have them repeated every three months. When this was done for the second time in Edinburgh a small TB lesion was identified in my left lung and, even though I had no symptoms, it was decided that I should return to Boston and start treatment. This was, of course, a great disappointment as well as a frightening development that could have destroyed my career—even my life. But fortunately antibiotic therapy for TB had just been developed and my lesion responded well after a few months of rest and medication.

Just before our departure from Edinburgh, I noted a startling change in how I was addressed by Sir James. On my arrival I had been addressed appropriately as *Doctor* Roe. Soon thereafter I was afforded the courtesy of being called *Mister* Roe, which is how surgeons are identified in the UK after qualification by the Royal College of Surgeons and thus was a recognition of my training. Later, as I developed friendships, I was known by my colleagues as "Ben" or "Benson." But now I had picked up a fourth identity as the professor addressed me simply as "Roe." At first it seemed to be a come-down and I was almost offended until someone pointed out that this was the ultimate compliment in that culture where the simple last name was used only for intimate and long-standing friends. It made me doubly sad to leave this delightful association.

Brief though the sojourn was, the memory of its value and pleasure remains. The friendships have continued to this day through correspondence and visits in both directions. Our children later visited some of those who had known them as infants in 1951. And several of the Royal Infirmary faculty, and subsequently their children, have visited us in San Francisco. It was an important chapter in our lives, socially and professionally, for which we have always been grateful.

An early photo of me in 1920 at two years old

My parents, Hall and Helene Roe, my brother George and
my sister Eleanore (I'm second from left). Approx. 1930

University California Varsity Crew National Champions
Kirk Smith, Chet Gibson, Stan Freeborn, Emil Bergh, Linton Emerson,
Dave de Varona, Stan Backlund, and Benson Roe

The 50th reunion of Poughkeepsie Champions in 1989

Los Angeles Examiner Sports

APRIL 22, 1939 CCC⊙ ⊙⊙   SECTION II **3**

Benson Roe "walks on water" as he was pushed during the
traditional ceremony of dunking coxswain Jim Dieterich
after defeating UCLA by five full lengths

U.S.S. Philadelphia

Certificate for crossing the equator on the U.S.S. Colorado
in 1937 in search of famed aviatrix Amelia Earhart

Sir Donald Douglas and Diana, one of my mentors
during the Moseley Fellowship in Edinburgh,
later to become Queen Elizabeth's surgeon

The Harvard Medical School

Resident surgeon, in front of the Bulfinch Building
of the Massachusetts General Hospital, 1950

Active duty as Lt. J. G. in the United States Navy, 1944

F.B. St. John, M.D., my father-in-law, who was chief of surgery at Columbia Presbyterian Hospital in New York City

Edward D. Churchill, M.D., Chief of surgery at MGH,
my principal mentor, who first labeled me as a Maverick

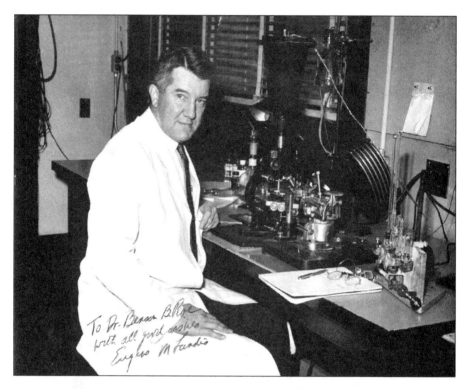

Eugene M. Landis, M.D.,Chairman, Dept of Psysiology, HMS,
who was my mentor during the National Research Fellowship
in his department in 1946

ROYAL MEDICAL SOCIETY
214th SESSION

ADDRESS

BY

BENSON B. ROE, M.D.

Surgeon, Massachusetts General Hospital, U.S.A.

WHO WILL SPEAK ON

"SURGICAL EDUCATION IN AMERICA"

AT

7 Melbourne Place
Friday, 19th January
At 8 p.m.

CAR PARK IN COUNTY SQUARE (St. Giles')

Royal Medical Society address in Edinburgh, 1951

Senior attending surgical staff at MGH who were my primary mentors
1st Row L-R Grantley W. Taylor, Edward D. Churchill, Joseph V. Meigs, and Leland S. Mc Kittrick
2nd Row L-R Richard H. Sweet, Robert R. Linton, Claude E. Welch, Marshall K. Bartlett and Oliver Cope

Julius Comroe, M.D., Director,
C.V.R.I, UCSF

Paul "Buck" Samson, M.D.

Sir James Learmoth, Chief of
Surgery University Edinburgh,
my mentor during the
Moseley Fellowship

Professor Leon Goldman,
Chairman of Surgery UCSF,
who appointed me

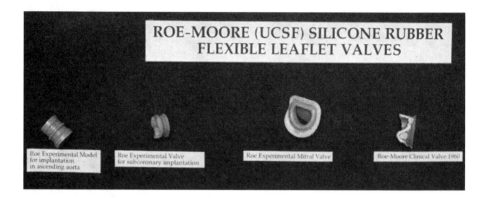

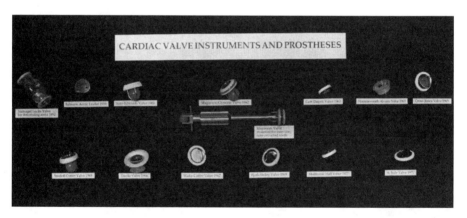

Various heart valve prostheses which were implanted during my career

The Artificial Heart. Shown is a calf in which the
device had been implanted five days previously.
Behind to the left is Paul Davis who designed and built it.
Center is Dr. Carlyle Smail who assisted me in
performing the implantation

My family
Jane, Me, my daughter Virginia, son David,
daughter-in-law Sukey, grandson Nathan and granddaughter Tessie

CHAPTER 13

Leaving Boston to Launch a Career

M ost people finish their formal education and training to face the real world in their twenties, before they become addicted to the security of institutional apron strings. Others break out into this reality after short terms of graduate education. But after four years of graduate school, followed by six years of hospital training interspersed with military service, a research fellowship and a traveling fellowship I found myself nearing my middle thirties with a small family before facing the challenge of making a living. I was thoroughly bonded to institutions; they were most of my identity. Being weaned from them was a daunting prospect and an essential metamorphosis.

I had left home to get professional education and always held the expectation of returning to pursue my career. I neglected to appreciate that those lucky competitors who were selected for the chief residency at the MGH were supposedly groomed to ascend the ladder to academic leadership. To eschew that pathway would be a waste of precious training. It was also shortsighted not to recognize how much I had grown fond of Boston, how many of my closest friends were there, and how much easier it might have been for my New York wife and Boston-born children to have stayed where we had a solid, if modest, future under the protective guidance of the Harvard/MGH community. To forsake that opportunity was certainly a folly which I had reason to regret on stressful occasions later on.

There was the other alternative of accepting my father-in-law's generous offer to work in his office at New York's prestigious Columbia-

Presbyterian Hospital. However, socially and economically advantageous though it would have been to latch onto Dr. St. John's carriage trade practice, I could not see myself living in New York City and being his satellite. I was very fond of him and respected him highly and I am certain that he would have been a strong and effective supporter, particularly since his only son had not gone into medicine. But that pathway did not fit my free spirit any more than being number three in Dr. Arthur Allen's office in Boston. There was also the guarded offer to join the group in Denver.

I just decided to follow my instinct to return home to San Francisco and carve out a living somehow. My rationale was an uninformed impression that the New England economy at that time was stagnant compared to the opportunities in a burgeoning California. Whether this choice was courageous, naïve, or foolish is a matter of opinion, but it did eventually work out. That Jane made no objection to this decision and offered no resistance to leaving her familiar environment and the proximity of her whole family is a tribute to her courage and devotion.

The precursor to that debut was a paycheck of $100 a month as chief resident surgeon at the MGH and the $300 a month stipend of the Moseley Fellowship in Edinburgh. The circumstances thus provoked a degree of panic as it became incumbent in our penniless state to assume a professional air of success among social contemporaries who had been climbing the corporate ladder for at least ten years.

The process started with my return to San Francisco in 1951 to start a private practice of surgery, having bravely or stupidly forsaken the security and prestige of the MGH and the familiarity of Boston medicine. Since I had little expectation of being kept busy with private patients and because of an attraction to the academic atmosphere I presented myself on the UCSF campus to volunteer for whatever role might be available. Apparently my trappings were acceptable enough to be given a clinical appointment as an Assistant Clinical Professor of Surgery with a munificent salary of $3000/yr. Significantly, I thus became the first and only member of the close-knit department in decades who was not a product of the UC training program. I hung out my shingle in an office downtown, which I subleased part time, and applied for surgical privileges in several hospitals. Although I encountered no difficulties in obtaining privileges to admit patients and to operate, it was another matter to surmount the "closed shop" attitude of a town totally dominated by the two medical schools, UC and Stanford, and to be accepted and have patients referred to me. Little by little, I built a modest practice in the usual surgical problems while concentrating on establishing a reputation in thoracic surgery by attending and participating in the chest service rounds. Seymour Farber, a pulmonary internist who was an HMS graduate, fed me a few patients and arranged an appointment for me on the chest service at the San Francisco County Hospital, where I gained considerable experience doing bronchoscopies (examining the windpipe and its branches through a long silver tube) and operating on tuberculous lungs, *pro bono*.

The first boost to my identity came one afternoon while seeing patients in my downtown office. A brusque phone call from Dan Delprat, the chief of surgery at St. Luke's Hospital, ordered me to drop what I was doing and look in on #3 operating room. He hung up without an explanation, but I thought it prudent to respect his authority, so I drove out to St. Luke's Hospital, changed my clothes and casually sauntered into #3 operating room. There I found a surgeon attempting to resect a lobe of lung. He was obviously sweating in serious difficulty, which the operating room supervisor had recognized and surreptitiously reported to the chief of surgery. My appearance had the desired result of being invited to scrub in to help out. The surgeon was obviously relieved and grateful to be bailed out of his problem, and the patient survived what would probably have been a fatal complication. I had simply done my duty as a Good Samaritan and gave no thought to any compensation or other consequences. The episode, however, resulted in an abrupt cancellation of that surgeon's chest surgery privileges and a recommendation to have those cases sent to me. This little bit of institutional tyranny was accomplished without protest or due process because it was the product of an authoritarian era. This established my identity as a thoracic specialist but it was accompanied by a veiled admonition to refrain from competing for the general surgical practice. I got only a few cases from this proclamation but it did help to build a reputation and to start some of the early heart operations in a friendly and supportive atmosphere, and St Luke's was only a segment of my practice.

Although I was an outsider to the local medical fraternity, my established San Francisco family and background were at least a little useful in opening some doors in starting practice. It was fortuitous that I volunteered to teach at UCSF where there was no serious competition to keep me effectively subordinated as would certainly have occurred had I gone to Stanford under Emil Holman and his protégé, Frank Gerbode who squeezed out two worthy competitors. It was not insignificant that my chosen field was in a burgeoning and wide open new specialty that had not yet developed a power establishment.

Undoubtedly, the most important element in my development was the acquisition of a strong and influential mentor from outside (across the bay). Paul "Buck" Samson was one of the small cadre who were trained at the University of Michigan in Ann Arbor by the pioneering John Alexander, who initiated the first, and for many years only, training program devoted exclusively to thoracic surgery. Buck's reputation was enhanced by his remarkable success in treating previously hopeless wounds of the chest during World War II. He settled in Oakland after the war and succeeded in establishing the politically difficult dictum that chest surgery would be practiced exclusively by surgeons with board certification in the subspecialty, a feat that has not been matched in San Francisco even to this day. He was the leading founder and first president of the Society of Thoracic Surgeons (STS) and one of the early directors of the new Board of Thoracic Surgery.

Buck was a huge man of 6'5" and 240 lbs, who had been a member of the US Olympic water polo team, but his formidable countenance was balanced by a genial smile and a gentle manner, which made him an effective leader. We had met and conversed at the national meetings of the American Association for Thoracic Surgery, which I attended faithfully, but how we got together was interesting. Early in my practice, a patient with a mediastinal (mid-chest) tumor was referred to me at Franklin Hospital in San Francisco and I had scheduled her for its surgical removal. One of her relatives, who was understandably uncertain about who I was and whether I was the right choice of surgeon, called Dr. Max Chamberlain, whom she knew in New York, for his opinion. His response was that the only surgeon on the West Coast she should consider was Paul Samson, who was immediately approached by the patient's family. When Buck telephoned me to ascertain the particulars of the case, I fully expected to have the patient transferred to him, which is what the family intended and what would have been proper. But instead of accepting the patient he graciously reassured the family and volunteered to come across the Bay and assist me to do the operation. This generous and unnecessary gesture was an important boon to my ego, my reputation and my pocketbook, not to mention his invaluable advice and help. He became a lasting friend and mentor. It was his influence that led to my appointment to the Board in 1971 and to my subsequent presidency of the STS. No such sponsorship was forthcoming from my UC colleagues, who were not happy about my invasion of their domain and would have gladly seen me drown.

During this period, I participated in the weekly Thoracic Outpatient Clinic at UCSF, its chest conference with the attending pulmonologists, and the cardiac conference with the attending cardiologists. It was thus that I gradually developed rapport with potential sources of surgical referrals in my specialty and was asked to participate in postgraduate teaching.

The Surgical Department's research laboratory was made available to me and I obtained a few small research grants from the university and from the local Heart Association to conduct some experiments, the fruits of which were the basis of papers that I presented at AATS meetings and later at the Society of Thoracic Surgeons. Among the important products of this work was the development of a flexible leaflet prosthetic heart valve out of silicone rubber in collaboration with David Moore in the UC Research and Development Lab. This device evolved slowly from meticulous machining of a pressure mold to produce 3 flexible leaflets of contour and strength enough to resist prolapse in the closed position but delicate enough to open widely with forward flow. Meticulous casting and testing were required to establish the parameters for optimal performance of the valve. Then it was necessary to obtain the material with the best durability and flexibility which entailed an exhaustive search through a myriad of elastomers (silicone rubbers), learning where to obtain them, how their properties were affected by pressure casting and then testing several of them to ascertain the best choice. Moore built a testing chamber that made the valves open and close something like sixty times a second to test durability. During this period of shop development various models were implanted in dogs to establish clinical feasibility. Finally, new molds were built to human dimensions and this valve was successfully implanted in a human patient in 1960. It was one of the first, along with five other experimental valves of different designs and materials that were successfully implanted in that year.

Thus I was able to establish a place on the national scene while my local practice gradually grew. My meager income improved slowly from under $4000 the first year to $9,000 in the second, and then to a level that could sustain a modest middle-class life style. After many moments of doubt about surmounting the obstacles I finally became convinced that I was here to stay. Jane had happily become accepted in her new city, easily making new friends of kindred background, establishing her identity in the Junior League, and gradually abandoning any yearning for New York. I renewed many of my old friendships and together we made new ones.

Without active sponsorship and likely referrals from internist colleagues it was necessary to hustle for a reputation and survival. This was accomplished by participating in the aforementioned conferences at UC and other hospitals, by volunteering to serve on committees (and later the boards) of the Heart Association, the American Cancer Society and the San Francisco Medical Society. These affiliations led to speaking opportunities and gradual recognition. San Francisco has always been a competitive venue because of its desirability as a place to live. That caused a huge influx of physicians who had been introduced to the Bay Area when it became a center of commerce and ship building and staging for the Pacific Theater during the war. So popular was the locale that promising members of the UCSF faculty rejected numerous attractive job offers with promotions just because they involved moving to the east or middle west. We all learned to recognize—as did I on leaving Boston—that the price of living in Northern California would be to sacrifice at least some opportunity. Many, who could easily have done well elsewhere, came here, confronted the competition, and eventually abandoned the effort. I was fortunate to survive.

CHAPTER 14

Heterodoxy— A Valuable Tool

Heterodoxy, defiance of orthodox thought, is the life blood of a maverick. On the one hand, many of history's greatest accomplishments have been the product of courageous, and sometimes outrageous, excursion off the beaten path to provide innovation and progress in commerce, politics, science, exploration, athletics and almost every other endeavor. On the other hand, those who dare to be heretics or even those who defy propriety are often spurned, rejected, or persecuted—up to burning at the stake. Even in the social tolerance of modern times pioneers are often considered foolhardy and meddlesome for disturbing the status quo.

Heterodoxy tends to be unproductive because it is likely to be disdained, outlawed, or ignored. The pioneer-heretic will address an issue that is interesting and/or controversial, but his effort will be in vain unless he is also in a position of enough power and recognition to withstand criticism and opposition, or unless he has sufficient wealth to pursue his quest without needing outside support. Those who acquire power and wealth are very likely to become enmeshed in orthodoxy with its financial security and peer approbation.

Heterodoxy was the cornerstone of cardiac surgery and it is lucky that I was comfortable with that attitude. The very subject was unorthodox because it was in surgery's "forbidden" realm. But the period immediately following World War II was one of explosive development and innovation. The time was right. The eagerness, energy and imagination of the young professional was enhanced with the maturity of being in the war.

This combination made it feasible to survive as a non-conformist while exploring a new field.

Of course, it is always arrogant to challenge and defy the status quo. Heterodoxy is meaningless when it stands alone as an annoyance. But when it stimulates the interest of the herd and evokes leadership it is acclaimed for its courageous stand. The trick is not just conjuring up the heterodox but rather selling it to others. That charm is the essence of political leadership. It is an art that I have only partially mastered. What brought me to the councils of power was diligence, along with skills of perception and innovation. But I have lacked the charm, the patience and the subtlety to evoke a supportive following. It has been my nature rather to be a confrontationist. My political accomplishments have resulted more from persistence and daring than from popularity.

It is interesting to consider what impels or drives one to become a maverick. Some are simply rebellious with an incentive to be different or to get away from the crowd. There is an inherent need to struggle for dominance; certainly all children and young animals display an impulse to be independent and to wander away, so discipline is required to keep them in the herd. Were it not for social pressures, most of us would behave in a random manner, perhaps to our great hazard. Certainly those whose environment imposes serious constraints or who suffer tyrannical repression have an incentive to break out of the mold. But what is the motivation of those, like myself, with comfort, security, identification, and at least some social loyalty to risk the disdain of their peers for the sake of a renegade thought? Who knows?

It was never my intent to rebel for its own sake. That is not a part of my personality and certainly I was not at odds with the establishment to which I belonged. Rather, I simply concluded that there were better ways to do things and was frustrated by their failure to come about. I was willing to ruffle a few feathers and/or be rejected in the process of promoting an improvement. And I had developed a fundamental antipathy for dogma and tyranny, so I had a natural resistance to any constraints that were imposed on my thoughts and objectives when those constraints are based on blind resistance to change. I was not as sensitive to the convictions and prejudices of others as I might have been in being outspoken and critical. There was no intent to alienate or defy, but inevitably the unconventional provokes antipathy.

The essence of a true scientist or investigator is the quest of new knowledge, which often requires the disproving of accepted doctrine or widely-held beliefs. The fervor with which some of those beliefs are grasped is sometimes astonishing, and when they are challenged by new information the believers may become irrationally defensive and resistant to an extent that prevents or delays the acceptance and utilization of a discovery. Occasionally and unpredictably, however, a new idea will be welcomed with instant and universal acceptance, either because the status quo had been uncomfortable or because the innovation had unusual appeal. I have experienced both of these reactions in response to my surgical contributions. Suffice it to say that heterodoxy played an important role in my professional career as well as my community life. It has resulted in no disastrous consequences perhaps because so many of my trappings were orthodox.

CHAPTER 15

Cardiac Surgeon

The dominant feature of my life, except perhaps for my wife, was being a cardiac surgeon. That was a role which, at its beginnings, was exciting, dramatic, challenging, frightening, and gratifying. It was true adventure. Its setting was ideal for one inclined to challenge convention because it was a virgin field with no doctrine to constrain new ideas. Indeed the very thought of cardiac surgery violated a doctrine that the heart was out of bounds for the surgeon. This attitude was based primarily on a 1925 report in *The New England Journal of Medicine* describing the disastrous results in a carefully planned series of surgical attempts to open obstructed mitral (heart) valves by the highly respected team of Elliot Cutler, chief or surgery at Boston's Peter Bent Brigham Hospital and Sam Levine, Chief of Medicine. There were other scattered reports in the medical literature of singular endeavors to operate on the heart but none had led to accepted practice or subsequent success. The heart had become the only remaining surgical frontier for the obvious reason that it was the only organ whose function was indispensable during any surgical intervention—much like the challenge of repairing an automobile engine with the necessity of keeping the motor running.

The foundations for surmounting this obstacle and opening a new era in cardiac surgery were: 1) the basic science of cardiac physiology that was just coming into its own to provide better understanding of how this previously mysterious organ functioned as well as how it responded to surgical trauma and stress; 2) the development of cardiac catheterization by Cournand and Richards (later to be Nobel Laureates) that provided functional information from inside the working heart with ongoing measurements of pressure and oxygen tension in the various chambers, from which

specific abnormalities can be identified, located, and quantified; 3) the desperation of operating on war wounds of the heart that met with unexpected and gratifying success; and 4) the persistence of those who pursued the
daunting challenge of building a heart-lung machine that would effectively
provide circulation and oxygenation while the heart was deactivated during
the repair process.

A structure was built on those foundations by a new and extraordinary generation of young surgeons, of which I was fortunate to be one.
These men were the first products of a new surgical era that emanated from
the six-year residency training programs begun at a handful of university
centers just before the war. Many of them had garnished their solid surgical training background with invaluable operative experience treating the
war wounded. Our (then) unique training and the maturing process of war
exposure generated a degree of confidence and independence that was well
beyond our years by traditional standards. Our predecessors, by contrast,
had been victims of an apprentice system that kept them subordinated and
deprived of meaningful experience for at least two decades after finishing
medical school. We were driven by bright horizons, and undaunted by protocol, full of youthful energy and imagination. And we were unrestrained
by the kind of bureaucratic regulation that currently curtails the clinical
application of spontaneous ideas until they have undergone exhaustive testing, often taking years.

Like pioneers of geographic exploration, we had no maps or guides,
no texts or teachers, no knowledge or special skills. We learned from our
mistakes, which we had been taught to acknowledge and examine in open
discussion. We learned from our imaginative and sometimes desperate
measures to salvage unexpectedly disastrous situations. Many, of course,
were unsuccessful but those that succeeded were triumphs. We learned
from our serendipitous discoveries, which we proudly shared with one
another at meetings, on the phone, and by visiting each other's operating
rooms. There were no secrets in this endeavor so an enormous amount of
information was exchanged through those channels, which facilitated
developing the specialty at lightning speed. Like all great advances, it came
about as a result of many factors and many people, not all of whom got the
credit they deserved. Although the historical background of the specialty
included a few isolated dramatic surgical forays dating as far back as the
turn or the century, its explosive growth and identity as a new specialty

occurred in little more than the decade between the mid 1950s to the mid '60s. It was an exciting period and being a part of it was a privilege, which I was too busy to appreciate at the time.

The initial procedures to work inside the heart were described as *closed* heart surgery, as opposed to *open* heart surgery. I have described this as the phase in which cardiac function is *sustained* during the operation. The first approach consisted of introducing a finger or instrument into the beating heart through a purse-stringed (leak-controlling) incision to force open a narrowed valve or obstruction. The first successful case using this method was reported in 1926—shortly after the *unsuccessful* series reported by Cutler and Levine—by London surgeon, Henry Souttar, who sadly related that he never repeated the feat because "No one sent me another case." It was not until 1946—just after World War II—that the procedure was resurrected by Charles Bailey in Philadelphia, Dwight Harken in Boston, and Lord Brock in London, each of whom performed and reported large series of successful cases. The operation was remarkably effective in most cases despite its blind and crude character, making the process breathtakingly uncertain. The process was remarkably forgiving because it amounted to a rough forceful poke of a finger against a thickly scarred valve in the blind hope that whatever tore open would (a) yield an adequate opening to relieve the obstruction and (b) retain enough valvular function to prevent significant regurgitation (back-flow). Amazingly it worked well enough to result in significant functional improvement in the vast majority of patients with low mortality rates.

A corollary to this sustained function technique was developed by Robert Gross at the Children's Hospital in Boston. It consisted of sewing a rubber sleeve to the low pressure atrial part of the heart, through which he made an incision to create a well through which it was feasible to close a hole between the atrial chambers by guiding sutures through the pool of blood by blind feeling. It was a dangerous technique of limited application but an interesting chapter in this developing field. These experiences demonstrated that the heart was a far more durable and resilient organ than we had been taught.

The second phase of *suspended* cardiac function, colloquially known as the *hypothermia* method, was initiated by Will Bigelow in Toronto, and also pioneered by Henry Swan in Denver, and F. John Lewis in Minneapolis, who shared the then unique experience of looking and working inside the living heart. That feat was accomplished by immersing the anesthetized patient in a bath of ice water to reduce the body temperature to hibernating levels, 30°–32° Celsius (86°–89° F.) The consequent reduction of metabolic activity allows the body, and most particularly the sensitive brain, to tolerate stopping the circulation for a brief period by shutting off the large veins that bring the blood into the heart (the superior vena cava and the inferior vena cava). The heart is allowed a few beats to empty before making an appropriate incision. That interval was sufficient to suture an abnormal opening between chambers or to incise a narrowed valve. Time constraints limited what could be accomplished and sometimes the job had to be cut short to maintain our self imposed limit of six minutes; it was a bit like operating with a gun in your back. Later we learned that the safety envelope was considerably longer, which is why we never had any neurological complications. This chapter was a valuable stepping stone and it provided a golden opportunity to become familiar with the inside of the living heart and to begin developing more complex corrective surgical procedures.

The ultimate achievement was to provide a *substitute* for the heart's function with a machine that took over its pumping function and oxygenated the blood, thus permitting access to the inside of the heart without strict time limitations. The heart-lung machine, which is the cornerstone of modern cardiac surgery, had been a dream for decades and its father, John Gibbon of Philadelphia, had worked on its development for over twenty years before using it successfully on the first patient. The big obstacle to this quest was finding a way to get oxygen into a volume of blood passing through the apparatus at a rate of two to three liters a minute. That feat is achieved in the human lung through tiny capillaries spread over the lung's combined alveolar (air sac) surface area of roughly 180 square feet, not easily duplicated in *any* apparatus.

Eager pioneers were struggling with these challenges in several institutions and in most cases their early forays into attempts with patients were fraught with tragedy and disappointment, usually for unknown reasons. Fortunately, there were enough successes to justify pushing on through the learning curve. My own role was at the fringe of this elite cadre of early cardiac surgeons because of the peculiar circumstances surrounding the endeavor at UCSF. My contemporary pioneering rivals who were to become famous included: John Kirklin at the Mayo Clinic, C. Walton Lillehei at the University of Minnesota, Henry Swan at the

University of Colorado, Albert Starr at the University of Oregon, Henry Bahnson at Johns Hopkins, Denton Cooley at Baylor, James Malm at Columbia, William "Harry" Muller at UCLA, Frank Gerbode at Stanford, and later, Norman Shumway. All were all firmly established protégés of powerful mentors who backed them with academic security and full institutional support. I, on the other hand, was a pretender as a part-time member of a department, in which I was an outsider, supporting myself with a modest down town private practice in general and thoracic surgery. At one point in the late 50's I held the title of Chief of Thoracic Surgery at three community hospitals, along with spending several hours a week in the laboratory at UC, attending and operating on the TB Service at the County Hospital and teaching at UC Hospital. It was a very busy time during which H. Brodie Stephens, Chief at UC, was doing a few early heart operations and open heart surgery was just beginning in various centers around the country, including Stanford, our cross-town rival.

The open-heart program at UCSF was very slow to get off the ground for various reasons, partly because Brodie Stephens did not have the benefit of either an intensive surgical training program or any scientific exposure. To his credit he worked hard and was doggedly determined, but his attempts to develop the necessary equipment and technical experience in the dog lab were disappointing. I was only one of four rivals from my generation who were eager to participate in the project in the hope of eventually succeeding to the leadership (the other three were all UC trainees). Because precedent dictated that my chances of eventually succeeding Brodie were essentially nil as an uninvited outsider I was less inclined to follow his leadership and looked instead for other opportunities. It was a period of mixed emotions because my competitive drive to explore new horizons was at odds with my choice to abandon Boston academia and do private practice instead. I became interested in the reports of those using hypothermia, so, at my own expense, I visited and watched Henry Swan in Denver and F. John Lewis in Minneapolis, in the hope of introducing their modality in San Francisco. Not surprisingly, the first clinical opportunity to apply this technique did not occur at UCSF but rather from Dr. Ann Purdy at Children's Hospital, who offered Roy Cohn of Stanford and me the joint opportunity to open a narrowed heart valve under hypothermia on a five year old child, thus launching my open-heart career through the back door. It is ironic that Ann Purdy was the wife of Dr. Emil Holman, Chairman of

Surgery and sponsor of Frank Gerbode at Stanford. Giving us this opportunity was demonstration of her professional independence.

The fickle trappings of fate associated with that episode unintentionally sealed my identity as a sub-specialist. The night before this dramatic first open-heart operation (which turned out to be one of the first two or three on the West Coast) I received a late night call from a pediatrician to operate on a child with appendicitis. Naturally, I begged off with apologies and explanations that were clearly intended to apply only to that circumstance. Nevertheless it triggered a disappearance of my general surgery referrals. This was a frightening consequence in my financially and professionally precarious state but by good fortune my thoracic practice continued to build and I marginally managed to survive.

It is hard to describe the drama and emotional pressure associated with the first episode of undertaking surgery inside the human heart, where surgeons had not theretofore dared to tread. Tough-ego surgeons are trained to repress their emotions but I will long remember that event and the excitement it generated. The patient was a child who had become increasingly cyanotic (blue) as the result of progressive narrowing of the valve at the outlet of the right ventricle. Her condition was serious but not imminently life threatening, which placed heavy moral pressure on the decision to subject her to a new and potentially dangerous procedure. We rehearsed the protocol in detail with acute awareness of the tight time restrictions on executing a process that we had never done before. She was anesthetized and immersed in a tub of ice water until her body temperature dropped to 31° Celsius (88° F), after which she was moved to the operating table and her chest opened. We placed tourniquet slings around her vena cavae. When all was in readiness the tourniquets were cinched and the heart allowed to empty. The pulmonary artery was quickly opened between previously placed retraction sutures and the tight valve incised to relieve its narrowing. It was a simple and short procedure by modern standards but it was the first time that I, and all those involved, saw and did something definitive inside of a living human heart without any detrimental consequence to the patient.

Even though Dr. Purdy's patient at Children's Hospital was the first one, it was UC's pediatric cardiologists, Mary Olney and Ellen Simpson, to whom I am eternally indebted for giving me a substantial and valuable opportunity to initiate open heart surgery at UCSF. They had gathered a large practice of children with congenital heart disease and had the courage and determination to subscribe to this new and obviously hazardous modality that offered the first chance for definitive correction of simple anomalies. Thus—without specific authorization—I initiated a series of successful open heart repairs at UCSF before the others were able to get started with the heart-lung machine. We did some forty odd cases of atrial septal defect closure, pulmonic valvotomy or aortic valvotomy with only three deaths and no complications from the arrested circulation. Across town at Stanford, Frank Gerbode was progressing and gaining the support of Stanford cardiologists, despite losing all of the first seven or eight open heart cases that he attempted with a locally built heart-lung machine.

Meanwhile, there was agitation about UC's inconsequential reputation in this burgeoning field, so Professor Leon Goldman, our surgical chairman, was quietly investigating candidates across the country to come and develop an effective program in heart surgery. By this time I had become intensely interested in the challenge but having given up my academic opportunities in Boston, my realistic hopes were limited to being just a participant with whomever was brought in. It never occurred to me that I would get the job in the seemingly hostile political setting where all appointments and support had long been bestowed exclusively on locally trained surgeons.

It was a complete surprise when Dr. Goldman called me into his office and unceremoniously asked me to undertake the responsibility to develop the cardiac surgery program at UCSF. This unlikely development caused great dismay to a partially displaced Brodie Stephens and to my eager local competitors, Orville Grimes, Richard Gardner and Bill Weirich. My elation dispelled any analysis of the reasoning, but in retrospect I can recognize a set of circumstances that probably gave me the advantage. My background, from the local perspective, was distinctive and perhaps even prestigious by virtue of a coveted surgical residency at the MGH under Pete Churchill and Richard Sweet, the leading lights in the primitive stages of clinical cardiothoracic surgery, my research fellowship in cardiovascular physiology at Harvard and my fellowship at the Royal Infirmary of Edinburgh, which exposed me to contrasting viewpoints and added a bit of éclat. These trappings, along with my successful start with heart surgery under hypothermia and my surgical performance in the outside hospitals, were likely considerations.

Needless to say, I was thrilled and delighted at the prospect. But fulfilling the challenge was another matter. I was fortunate to be given the opportunity but it was late in getting started against the competition and fraught with political conflict. I realized that it must have been a very difficult decision for Dr. Goldman because it circumvented the standing chief, Brodie Stephens, his colleague and close personal friend as well as the other three young contestants who were insiders, trained in his department. This made my position awkward. Although I can understand the reluctance of this kind hearted man to embarrass the others whom he had seemed to betray, he may not have realized that this challenging task was more difficult because there was no formal announcement about my appointment. That omission effectively deprived me of any political clout to organize the faculty and spared my resentful competitors of any need to be accountable to me.

It was an exciting opportunity in a difficult situation that required assuming authority and initiative with a mandate that was vague and undocumented. Surgical residents were assigned to a newly identified service and we were off and running with a team that quickly learned to work well together on a daily basis in both the operating room and the experimental laboratory. Hospital Administration was cooperative in providing a dedicated operating room, a three-bed ward for post operative management (which I—and perhaps others—dubbed "Intensive Care"), and most of the needed equipment. This innovation was necessary because the special duty nurses who had traditionally cared for critically ill patients had little or no experience with complexities of postoperative cardiac problems and many had proven to be unreliable.

The rapid development of this dramatic new specialty was inherently fraught with pitfalls that offset its triumphs, not only in the formidable hazards and monumental ignorance of a new clinical science but also in the political arena which was darkened by resentment and skepticism. Unless those upon whom one's reputation rides are committed to supporting one's travails and forgiving the inevitable failures, one's destiny is grim. Such a commitment derives either from personal faith and friendship or from administrative authority that exerts pressure on referral sources and local gossip. In my case, the unprecedented appointment of an outsider to a coveted role was offensive to those insiders who considered themselves to be comparable or superior candidates. Furthermore, the introduction of a new service into the system generated a broader resentment by requiring others to give up bed space, an operating room and office space. And the recognition of cardiothoracic surgery as a separate specialty was understandably unpopular with the general surgical faculty and resident staff, who had traditionally considered this field to be part of their domain, they did not wish to relinquish. Added to the resistance of my surgical colleagues was the innate conservatism of the academic cardiologists who considered cardiac surgery to be experimental and thus not suitable fare for any but the most desperate and hopeless patients that were the highest operative risks. Institutional loyalty has never been a strong tradition at UC so most of the cardiologists felt no obligation to promote the new specialty. When they had a patient who was a surgical candidate they had no hesitation about sending him/her elsewhere for whatever reason that occurred to them, one of which was dealing with me as an outsider. The negative consequences were cumulative; rumors of incompetence and bad results were circulated without any attempt to investigate the facts objectively. That I survived is a miracle; that my ambitions were frustrated should not be surprising.

The good fortune of having the support of the Olney/Simpson team in providing pediatric patients was offset by the misfortune of encountering other personalities who were integral to my success but whose hostility or disloyalty was destructive to building the service and expanding our practice. Leon Goldman certainly did nothing to hinder my progress but he was so busy with his own administrative problems that he had no awareness of my struggles and no time to be involved. But the lack of a powerful mentor using his authority to curb the detractors and actively support the struggle of developing a new specialty was a handicap that kept me behind my competitors. Of course, it occurred to me that my problems may be the product of my own deficiencies which we tried to scrutinize at our weekly review conferences and by comparisons with published results elsewhere. These evaluations kept my conscience clear but were ineffective in refuting destructive gossip.

The unique aspect of this pioneer undertaking was its being so conspicuous. Most hazardous exploration is conducted in remote or private surroundings in which failures and mishaps are unseen and success is measured only if and when one reaches the finish line. But cardiac surgery was front page news and every step was under critical scrutiny by skeptics, by rivals and by potential sponsors. Tragedies were inevitable in this treacherous sea of ignorance and their consequences were pivotal in providing fodder for the critics. Thus it was essential to have all possible overt support, especially from one's leader and medical colleagues. Survival of this highly competitive endeavor was largely dependent on which of these forces prevailed. Progress often represented the fringe of morality in that clinical situations put us in the position of having to try untested modalities that were beyond the bounds of orthodox surgical teaching. Those that worked were occasionally credited to the discoverer, if he took the trouble to report it; but those that didn't were arguably irresponsible. As mentioned before it is certain that cardiac surgery would not exist today if that developmental era had been constrained by current testing requirements of the Federal Drug Administration. Many of the most important advances in the safety and capabilities of modern cardiac surgery were the result of adopting unproved methods.

The first mechanical (Gibbon) oxygenator to be used clinically was a crude, inefficient and expensive apparatus which had to be primed with twelve to sixteen pints of freshly drawn heparinized blood. It was a stainless steel box in which the blood was cascaded down ten vertical stainless steel screens immersed in an oxygen atmosphere, but so inefficient that most of the flow had to be recycled to absorb enough oxygen. Although this machine was a major breakthrough that permitted longer access to the open heart, the mortality from these procedures was very high, particularly if the bypass lasted for more than an hour. The deaths occurred, rarely in the operating room but usually five to ten days later, from heavily congested lungs, the explanation for which was obscure. It was not appreciated that severe changes were occurring in the circulating blood, despite meticulous cleaning of the apparatus to eliminate foreign antigens and pyrogens (proteins that cause fever) and careful measures to minimize mechanical damage to the blood by the machinery.

The real explanation for these mysterious and vexing deaths, after what seemed to be a smoothly executed procedure, evolved only in retrospect when almost miraculous benefits were derived from the adoption of two modalities, both of which defied conventional knowledge and logic. First, was the development of a bubble oxygenator by Dick DeWall, constructed from simple, readily available plastic tubing. This apparatus became widely accepted, despite its being theoretically unsafe by introducing potentially lethal blockage of capillaries with bubbles, particularly in vital tissues such as the brain. Its primary virtues were to achieve far more efficient oxygenation without requiring recirculation and to reduce the priming volume by more than seventy-five per cent, which reduced cost and minimized procurement problems. In addition, was its easy and inexpensive availability and its disposability that eliminated the problem of removing foreign protein from previous use. But the main benefit of this method was not initially recognized. Postoperative lung complications and mortality were both dramatically reduced. This gratifying result was the result of fewer blood interactions, but at the time it was just serendipity that these virtues were combined with the second equally heretical modality, namely hemodilution (see below), which further reduced the need for blood in the priming fluid. The important consequence was that blood reactions were either minimized or obliterated. This development was a significant contradiction to the lore of blood transfusion, which had never been challenged as a safe and effective modality while being credited with saving many lives on both the battlefield and in the operating room. The era of tissue transplantation and its problems with tissue rejection had not yet arrived. Thus when Bill Neptune of Boston was courageous (some would say irresponsible) enough to try priming his pump-oxygenator with only bloodless saline solution (thus greatly diluting the red cells) he was considered a heretic because it was universally accepted that anemia (low red blood count) was detrimental and life threatening. Yet this drastic and seemingly counterproductive step turned out to be directly responsible for significantly diminishing the high rate of unexplained complications and deaths associated with early extracorporeal circulation. And contrary to expectations it was not detrimental to oxygen delivery but actually *improved* the blood flow through the capillaries by reducing the blood viscosity. It was not initially appreciated that two surgical conditions in heart operations, (a) non-pulsatile flow from roller pumps and (b) the *increased* viscosity of the blood caused by body cooling, both tended to impair flow through the capillaries[viii]. Thus this "inappropriate" innovation turned out to have an unexpected fringe benefit along with its fundamental improvement. While hemodilution was not my brain child, I was attracted to its potential benefits and we were among the first to adopt this "foolish" concept, for which we initially received considerable criticism. But our results improved significantly when we did and its safety was verified[ix x].

Paradoxically, it was the Jehovah's Witnesses who indirectly contributed to the proof of this off the wall modality. Their adamant religious interdiction against the administration of blood under any circumstances was initially a barrier against considering them as candidates for open heart surgery because it simply couldn't be done without several units of blood. When someone had the courage to undertake this impossible challenge the result was to make the patients alarmingly anemic after not only priming the system but also replacing all of the surgical blood loss with saline solution. To everyone's surprise the patients not only survived the procedures but their course was smoother and less complicated than the usual patient who was given blood. Thus the heretical concept of deliberate hemodilution was substantiated. The contradictory success of this modality can now be attributed to obviating the incipient interactions of imperfect blood matches, which is akin to rejection in organ transplantation.

Our experience with primitive hypothermia (temporary strangulation) heart surgery turned out to be safer and less complicated than using the early screen oxygenators with large blood primes. It was not until the introduction of hemodilution that procedures performed with the heart-lung machine achieved comparable morbidity and mortality rates.

Progress was not always the product of surgical courage or ingenuity. The first oxygenator that we used clinically was the cumbersome screen type, whose priming volume I tinkered with laboriously to reduce from sixteen units (of blood) to thirteen. The result was of imperceptible benefit. Commercialization of the bubble oxygenator had not yet occurred but was in development by the Travenol Laboratories, who sent us a shipment of disposable units they had developed, made in the form of a welded pathway between 2 layers of vinyl sheeting, to test in our animal studies. It was a bonanza because it saved the enormous effort and expense of running the large screen oxygenator and greatly diminished the terrible sacrifice of dogs for priming blood. We were pleased with its performance and looked forward to its availability in the clinical version. Then one day Betty Swenson, our pump technician (now called a perfusionist), declared that we were having better results with our dogs than with our human patients and, therefore, we should use this oxygenator in the operating room. Betty was a remarkable woman with degrees in nursing and engineering who had marvelous mechanical skills. Her contributions were numerous in those days of rapid development but the importance of her influence may never have emerged had my matriarchal background not taught me to heed the voice of a strong-minded woman. She was a tremendous asset to our team both for her performance and for her innovative ideas. I always listened to her and usually accepted her recommendations, but this time it could not be because the product had not been approved and there was sign, sealed between the layers of plastic, that clearly read: FOR EXPERIMENTAL USE ONLY—NOT FOR HUMAN CONSUMPTION. I should have been suspicious when Betty uncharacteristically argued only briefly with my refusal because the next morning I walked into the operating room to do a relatively simple heart repair and found the "experimental" plastic bag oxygenator primed, connected to the perfusion tubing and ready to go—in direct disobedience of my order. I was vexed and the ensuing discussion was a lively interchange. The legal and moral grounds of my position were counterbalanced with the evident superiority of this unauthorized modality, plus the practical fact that the appropriate alternative—the clunky screen oxygenator—could not be quickly assembled nor could its required thirteen units of fresh, heparinized blood prime be obtained for that day's surgery. Anyhow, I had learned that it is nearly impossible to win an argument with a determined woman, so I capitulated.

The result, of course, was a smooth case and an uncomplicated recovery, which persuaded me to abandon the screen oxygenator and to use the Travenol bags for all cases thereafter. The experimental model was soon supplanted with an approved human model and we enjoyed a dramatic improvement in surgical morbidity and mortality.

The dire consequences and high mortality of our primitive endeavors in this field were often mysterious and our progress toward improvement was frequently the product of serendipity, such as I just described. It meant that we were constantly groping for answers with desperate measures or accidentally discovering solutions. It was usually either necessary or inevitable that the hearts we were operating on would spontaneously fibrillate (diffuse ineffective twitching instead of regular contraction). When we were finished a direct current electric shock would be administered to stop the fibrillation and restore normal contraction, which usually took place after one or two attempts. But sometimes, this measure did not work; the heart would either not respond at all to the shock or would beat a few times and then keep reverting to fibrillation to result in a fatality. Needless to say this occurrence is a devastating conclusion to what had seemed to be a flawless procedure and a perfect performance of the pump-oxygenator. On one occasion, I defibrillated a heart eighty-four times before it remained stable in a regular rhythm and the patient survived uneventfully; all the surgical team were convinced that it was a futile effort after the first ten or fifteen attempts and were dismayed at my obstinacy. Another time, after a long and difficult coronary bypass procedure, the patient's heart was so weak that it would not respond to any of the usual stimulating medications and it was impossible to discontinue the pump. After more than an hour of trying every possible measure I finally conceded defeat and stepped back from the table to remove my gloves. As I did so Bill Hamilton, the anesthetist, made a final gesture in desperation by injecting a massive bolus of adrenaline, many times the maximum, and the patient amazingly recovered. She lived another ten years during which I was undeservedly rewarded with frequent crates of artichokes from her farm in Santa Cruz. These events, though unusual, were distressing and unexplained outcomes of what should have been uneventful procedures.

That last big hurdle to surgical safety was mastered with the adoption of cardioplegia ("heart paralysis"), which was instrumental in reducing the risk of heart surgery into the category of common general surgical procedures. During open-heart operations the heart's function is necessarily suspended and the circulation to the rest of the body is maintained by the heart-lung machine. But the circulation to the heart itself usually has to be interrupted by clamping the first section of the aorta; from which the coronary arteries emerge. Consequently, the heart muscle either must have its blood supply provided through a separate pathway or suffer the consequences of suffocation. The solution was to pump blood through small tubes inserted into the coronary artery openings, which had been standard practice up until the early 1970s. Logical and sustaining though this practice appeared to be, there was a small but undeniable incidence of unexplained deaths from irreversible cardiac spasm, called "stone heart," which occurred after the aortic clamp was removed and the heart's normal circulation restored. This distressing and invariably fatal occurrence provoked me to review Shumway's apparently safe method of isolating the heart by cooling it with immersion in an ice-cold saline solution. While he reported good results with this approach, it was cumbersome and messy by spilling fluid out of the operative field onto the floor so it occurred to me that its cooling objective could be achieved more rapidly, more evenly and more efficiently by infusing an ice cold solution *into* the cardiac tissue through the coronary circulation instead of pouring *onto* the outer surface of the heart. I was also aware that the hibernating effect of cooling would be augmented by paralyzing the heart with potassium solution to minimize metabolic activity. Potassium had formerly been used and abandoned because, although it did stop the heart it resulted in long term damaging effects on the heart muscle tissue[xi]. But recent animal studies had revealed that lower concentrations of potassium were safe and effective, without damaging consequences, which we confirmed to our satisfaction in the laboratory.

In a dangerous act of faith I decided to combine the methods by using a single infusion of nearly frozen solution containing a mild concentration of potassium which both cooled and stopped the heart in a relaxed state while it was being operated on, thus abandoning the accepted standard of maintaining a separate infusion into the coronary arteries. To our delight and surprise this technique, which was called cardioplegia, appeared to protect the heart from damage for two hours or more without receiving any blood supply whatsoever. When I first reported our preliminary results informally at a national scientific meeting it was considered to be so unconventional, illogical and heretical as to border on malpractice. However, when we formally presented the data demonstrating the remarkable results of the first 105 cases our paper was well accepted and the technique spread with remarkable rapidity, and was soon acclaimed as the modality of choice[xii]. This then became the third major innovation that caused cardiac surgery to emerge from the realm of mystery and hazard to the level of mortality and morbidity enjoyed by ordinary surgical procedures. Indeed it was said that it had allowed slow and clumsy surgeons to get as good results as the fast and famous.

Almost every newly proposed clinical procedure provokes controversy and becomes accepted or rejected only gradually after skeptical trial and critical evaluation, which was certainly true about hemodilution. But for some reason, cardioplegia attained almost instantaneous acceptance around the world and amazingly was never disputed as a valuable tool, despite its defiance of the fundamental logic that maintaining circulation (to the heart) should be safer and more reliable than shutting it off. Indeed in the two years following our formal introduction of the technique there were 165 papers in the English language literature on the subject of cardioplegia, none of which disputed its value and efficacy and all of which dwelt on measures to improve either the formulation or the technique. It was our most important contribution to surgical science. But we never participated in the subsequent deluge of papers on the subject with the result that our role in its initiation has largely been forgotten.

In sharp contrast to the foregoing scenario of acceptance was my serendipitous discovery of another modality which proved to be effective in saving fourteen lives on my service, but which has received virtually no recognition or acceptance[xiii]. Many years ago, I was operating on a patient with classical clinical manifestations of an obstructed mitral valve, which it was not considered necessary to verify with the relatively unsophisticated diagnostic technology of the time. In those days, the mitral valve was routinely opened with finger manipulation instead of with more dangerous open heart surgery; thus the patient was unceremoniously operated upon for "blind" mitral valvotomy. Upon introducing my finger into the left atrium I discovered, to my surprise and dismay, that the valve was normal but a large tumor was almost filling the chamber and partially blocked the valve orifice—thus mimicking the effect of a stenosed (narrowed) valve. To remove it obviously required opening the heart and thus the use of the heart-lung machine, which then could not be made immediately available. It was, therefore, appropriate to close the patient and plan on returning another day. But it occurred to me that in planning the second approach it would be useful to know how and where the tumor was attached. So I swept my finger around to probe atrial cavity,—and disaster struck! I had unintentionally dislodged the tumor from its fragile pedicle, rendering it a floating ball-valve, which totally obstructed the mitral valve whenever my finger was withdrawn from holding the tumor away from the opening. This presented the worst kind of dilemma. Removing my finger spelled certain death. And the alternative of opening the atrium to extract the tumor could be expected to result in a massive and uncontrollable hemorrhage with the same tragic outcome. I chose the latter course in the faint and desperate hope that the bleeding could somehow be stemmed. So I made an incision next to my finger and quickly removed it while squeezing the heart with my other hand. Out popped the tumor, and with it a gush of blood that quickly filled the chest so as to submerge and obscure the heart. It appeared that all was lost and that nothing could be done to save the patient. While I stood there helpless and despondent the blood level surprisingly began to recede and the heart gradually emerged into view as the standing blood was removed by the suction tubes. We saw the heart to be in a stationary state

of ventricular fibrillation (ineffective beating), thus arresting the hemorrhage. With this fortuitous exposure I quickly clamped and sewed up the
hole in the atrium, after which it was a simple matter to shock the heart into
regular rhythm. The patient survived uneventfully and lived for many years.

This experience led me to recognize the potential value of *deliberately*
fibrillating the heart when a surgeon encountered massive hemorrhage from
a bleeding source that was obscured in a pool of blood and there was no
support from a heart-lung machine. Thus I made it a routine to have the
electrical apparatus to induce fibrillation available on the operating table for
every open chest procedure involving the heart or major vessels where massive hemorrhage was a possibility. As a result I had the opportunity to arrest
the circulation with fibrillation on several occasions, each of which resulted
in salvaging a hemorrhaging situation that seemed to be hopeless, and none
of which resulted in brain damage or other complication. This experience
was published but, despite its complete success in saving lives, there has
been virtually no acceptance or wide usage of the method. Presumably it is
because surgeons are reluctant to administer a deadly modality (fibrillation)
or because they are not convinced that having it always available for a rare
occurrence is worth the trouble. The reliability and effectiveness of the measure is dependent on virtually instantaneous application so as to arrest the
circulation *before* massive exanguination occurs, which does not allow time
to have the apparatus brought to the operating table and connected.

Another valuable modality that I introduced and that never received
much acceptance was the process of melting suture knots, which came from
my sailing experience. The commonest postwar marine cordage was made
from polyester [Dacron] that melts when heated. A soldering iron is routinely used for severing the line and simultaneously sealing the ends from
fraying. Dacron also proved to be the strong and durable suture of choice
for implanting heart valves but its "memory" (stiffness) characteristics made
the knots tend to untie, the prevention of which required five or six throws
and relatively long ends for security, the result of which was a crown of tas-
sels on the valve. It occurred to me that the suture knots could be heat severed and welded together after no more than three throws, which would
both save time and significantly reduce the amount of exposed suture material. I found a pencil sized soldering iron that could be sterilized and used
on the operating table. Paul Kelly, one of my trainees, and I published this
technique after careful testing to verify that the process did not diminish

knot strength. It gained a few enthusiastic followers but the idea has faded into oblivion despite its convenience and simplicity, not to mention its secondary benefit of reducing clot formation on the prosthetic valve[xiv].

These are mere samples of a multitude of technical innovations that sped the progress of the new specialty from its crude, ignorant, treacherous beginnings to a highly sophisticated, scientifically managed, and safe modality. In the space of less than twenty years, the role of surgery in the treatment of heart disease emerged from virtually zero to essentially 100%. That dramatic metamorphosis resulted in a surgical opportunity for palliation or cure for *every* form of cardiac disease or abnormality, whereas before World War II cardiac surgery did not exist. No other aspect of surgery has emerged so rapidly and to such total dominance of what had been a medical field. To have participated in that exciting transition was my great good fortune.

The influence and contribution of my residents was a significant element in every step of the way. The most dramatic example of that impact was just after the advent of cardiac transplantation, which had been meticulously developed by Norman Shumway at Stanford in preparation for human use, only to have the first patient done by Christiaan Barnard in Capetown shortly after visiting Shumway to learn the technique. The enormous publicity that attended its introduction and its dramatic appeal provoked scores of cardiac surgeons to jump on the bandwagon before the management hazards had been worked out. Denton Cooley was among the most eager and did some twenty-two transplants, all of whom died in a matter of weeks or months, despite surviving a successful surgical procedure. I chose to avoid this temptation partly because we had no team interested in the immunological aspects of the problem and also because of Shumway's proximity thirty miles down the road. It seemed ridiculous to compete against his superb and experienced team. To fend off the barrage of inquiries and provocation that came from every direction, I responded that I would consider a transplant only when the circumstances were compelling and the chances of long-term success were favorable. The technical procedure is simple, despite its dramatic overtones, and the challenge lies in exercising a meticulous regimen to avoid organ rejection. To keep the issue at bay, I stipulated six difficult criteria to be fulfilled and was confident that I would be spared the challenge by this obstacle. Then one night, my resident Lloyd Rudy interrupted my dinner to announce that he had found a patient who met the criteria. My best efforts to disqualify either the donor or the recipient were unsuccessful, and I found myself obliged to fulfill a promise that I had no desire to face. It was a dramatic evening of arranging the proper permits, gathering the members of two operating teams (one to remove the donor heart and the other to implant it in the recipient), transferring the fifty-four-year-old brain-dead donor, who had been the victim of an automobile accident, from the San Francisco County Hospital to UCSF. Because I deplored the sensationalism associated with the transplant effort I attempted to do the procedure surreptitiously under a false listing in the middle of the night but failed to avoid publicity. Fortunately the procedure went well despite our inexperience and the patient recovered uneventfully and lived for seven years. I never did another one.

All of this activity in a somewhat frenetic setting was possible only because of the team whose participation was essential to every phase of our progress. John Hutchinson, another HMS graduate, was our surgical cardiologist whose presence and sound wisdom were frequently crucial in the operating room as well as in patient management and in objective evaluation of our work. John is the most sensible and practical internist I have ever known. I always respected his opinion and have been grateful for his sound judgment in difficult and stressful situations. Betty Swenson could be relied upon completely in a crisis. Her calm was epitomized in an episode in the middle of an open heart procedure when I heard a crash of broken glass followed by stopping the pump, which, of course, is what keeps the patient alive while the heart is open. Heart surgeons necessarily learn never to get panicky but the specter of a dead patient on the operating table is sufficiently disconcerting to ask what had happened. Betty's response was a calm and polite, but firm, "You take care of your business and I'll take care of mine." After a brief interlude, the pump was working again and the patient did well. After it was over she told me that a bottle of solution had fallen into the roller pump where it was crushed and shards of glass had ruptured the tubing. With her typical cool she had quickly stopped the pump, clamped the tubing, replaced the torn segment, evacuated the air, and resumed the circulation in a time frame that subjected the patient to no harm—no mean feat! Betty's successor was Madeline Massingale who was similarly reliable and helpful in coping with problems. William K. "Bill" Hamilton, Walter "Skip" Way, and Neri Guidani were among several skilled anesthetists who played crucial roles in managing complex problems of drug administration, fluid balance and monitoring, all of which were essential to the successful outcome of a complex procedure. A succession of scrub nurses, including Sandy Rodrigo, provided support at the operating table, often anticipating what I needed before it was asked for. And most underrated are the residents who were skillful assistants and surrogate managers without whom I could not have functioned. They were the source and/or the critics of many innovations. These bright young men, each of whom worked with me virtually every day for two years, have been the source of great pride to me. All have gone on to successful and productive careers. A list of their names appears in Appendix B.

Research was the cornerstone of our endeavor during that period. Curiosity is the motivating stimulus for research and it stems from a critical attitude toward everything done in a constant quest for improving results. Cardiac surgery was particularly conducive to investigation because so many disappointments lacked explanation. The high mortality in its early phases provoked many of us to try desperate and often potentially dangerous measures that could never be justified in today's regulated setting.

These were exciting, stimulating and rewarding times in spite of the disappointments and failures of a hazardous undertaking and in spite of political vicissitudes. I was lucky to have had that opportunity. As time progressed, of course, the challenges became less acute, the procedures became more standardized, and the pressure diminished significantly. It would, however, be misleading to suggest that progress came to a halt at this juncture. A huge influx of sophisticated technology and the innovative talents of bright surgeons have continued to provide enormous advances in the scope and safety of cardiac surgery. But the sense of adventure gradually faded away and it was no longer an important requirement for the cardiac surgeon to be innovative and courageous at the operating table.

Of course it was fun to participate in the evolution of the important modality of cardiac surgery from almost a dare devil undertaking into a safe, reliable procedure now being performed thousands of times every day. The label "cardiac surgeon" has long lost its aura of drama to take its place along with scores of other specialists, but I am proud of having participated in its initial significance.

CHAPTER 16

The Surgical Personality

The old expression, "Occasionally wrong, but never in doubt" is how my wife refers to me in moments that seem to require apologetic explanation of my behavior. Arrogant and degrading though it may appear, I realize that she is right and that her expression is an appropriate definition of the surgical personality. Generalities always have exceptions but most non-surgical physicians enjoy the protective luxury of careful consideration and judicious trial of their diagnostic and therapeutic decisions. Most surgeons, on the other hand, are committed to a course of action that involves some degree of brinkmanship, exposing them to an unexpected crisis where decisive action is mandatory. Outcome is likely to depend on making the right choice from two or more alternatives—and making it rapidly. Inevitably, some of these decisions will be wrong—often at the price of a human life. A surgeon must have a durable character, both psychologically and professionally, to survive those errors, a determination to persist in a quest for success, and an imagination to provide solutions.

The public's image of the surgeon's virtue is that of manual dexterity. In reality only a few surgical procedures require extraordinary technical skill whereas the decision of how, when and where to apply that skill can be the crucial factor in success or failure. Many football quarterbacks can throw long and accurate passes but it takes a wise and quick witted quarterback to call the best plays and to make that split-second choice of the most likely pass receiver.

This characteristic is, of course, less important in routine and non-critical surgical procedures but in the early days of heart surgery, where the wrong choices and slow decisions had a good chance of being fatal, it was essential. Whatever success I achieved in my field was significantly relat-

135

ed to that ability. In its developmental stages, cardiac surgery was the epitome of daring exploration that called on imagination and innovation to solve problems, courage and resourcefulness to try the unproved, and fortitude to withstand the criticism of deprecators when endeavors were not successful. None of these characteristics were my conscious identities but in retrospect all were essential to success and survival in that era.

It was a unique time in the history of surgical development because it contradicted the established and protective doctrine of guiding and mentoring young and inexperienced surgeons by their seasoned elders. But the elders lacked any knowledge or experience in this new field so they either provided the critique and support of their experience in other fields or just left us to our own resources. We were like children thrown into the deep water to sink or swim. Only a few were fortunate to have the guidance and day-to-day support of a wise and respected mentor such as Richard Varco, a master surgeon who worked closely but inconspicuously with Walt Lillehei in Minneapolis, and Alfred Blalock, the pioneer of the "blue baby" operation, who did the same for Henry Bahnson in Baltimore. But these mentors had already established their reputations and did nothing to diminish the credit that accrued to the new generation. These relationships undoubtedly had their tense moments and I don't regret the opportunity to set my own course, despite its perils. There was no lack of confidence in the cadre of vigorous young surgeons who plunged into this new field because of their exceptional training and maturity in the military. We had been trained to make difficult decisions, to subject ourselves to strict self criticism, and not to be devastated by our inevitable mishaps. Progress in cardiac surgery required mastery in all of the above; it was filled with uncertainties that needed decisive action and with disappointments that needed constructive scrutiny.

It is fitting that I elected to undertake sailing as an avocation when the financial opportunity arose. The choice was partially due to a friendship with Frank and Marion Hinman, both of whom were experienced sailors, who were looking for a partner in the purchase of a new boat, and who turned out to be superb mentors. It was also realistic that my academic and practice responsibilities encompassed every Saturday morning, so as to preclude golf as a recreation, whereas afternoons were ideal for sailing. Because San Francisco Bay is consistently windy and foggy in the summer months and because the local geography, unlike the Atlantic coast, is frequently inhospitable for leisurely social cruising, much of the Bay sailing population were driven to racing for lack of interesting alternatives and it became the most popular activity. And also unlike the East Coast, the every day winds are usually brisk enough to make the process challenging, exciting, even stressful. In winds of more than thirty knots, most sensible sailors in the rest of the world wouldn't think of using a spinnaker, but here the competition is so keen and daring that we would all try it at the cost of a wild and treacherous ride. The sport was ideal for a cardiac surgeon's busman's holiday—strenuous, dangerous, demanding of quick decision and rampant with potential for serious error. I loved it even though it provoked more dry mouth and sweaty palms than doing heart surgery. Not only did the excitement of racing appeal to me but also I enjoyed the mechanics of maintaining and operating the boat to achieve optimal performance. Although I never attained much success on the racing circuit we derived a great deal of enjoyment in the process. Having our boat berthed at the San Francisco Yacht Club in Belvedere, on the protected north side of the bay in Marin County, was an added pleasure because there was always a pocket of afternoon sun on an otherwise fog shrouded bay where we could dry the sails, rehash the race and quench our thirst. These moments provided indulgence and satisfaction at their best.

Sailing proved to be a useful testing ground for prospective residents who sought an appointment in our training program. Sailing skill shares with surgical skill the ability to recognize and solve problems rapidly, far more important than factual knowledge and intellectual brilliance. Among the best and most effective of my various racing crews were some who had never been on a sailboat before, but who recognized how things worked, quickly observed a problem arising, and instinctively found a mechanical solution. The best of them learned rapidly, only needed to be told once about how to do something, and were reliable in a crisis. In contrast, were some who supposedly had vast sailing experience and verbalized great technical knowledge but who were so confused and clumsy in a crisis that I wanted to throw them overboard. The former make the best surgeons; the latter belong somewhere else.

Surgeons enjoy each other's company the same way as do members of a professional football team. They necessarily have strong egos and thick skins. The thoracic surgical conventions of the late '50s and early

'60s were circuses of daring exploits, unbridled criticism and heated controversy. Claims of spectacular achievement were common but critical and skeptical commentaries deflated any hubris. Everyone went home from these meetings to change at least some aspect of his routines in a constant quest for better results in an endeavor that remained full of pitfalls. A crucial element in our rapid progress was the absence of secrecy about either methods or results. Professional ethics precluded any thoughts of patenting our innovations. We all learned from each other's successes and failures in an atmosphere of mutual support and exchange of ideas. In today's world of governmental restrictions and rampant litigation this scenario could never occur. Any lives that might have been spared by restraining innovation have been offset a thousand fold by the lives that are credited to the daily products of hospital colleagues held us accountable for our actions and certainly our success was measured by the avoidance of disaster. However, exploration is inherently hazardous and making it safe is an oxymoron.

A footnote to living in the world of surgical personalities is the consequence of inadvertently imposing those expectations on one's family and lay friends who may be offended by the seeming arrogance of such certitude. That is a price we have to pay.

CHAPTER 17

The Artificial Heart Project

O ne of my favorite talks on the development of cardiac surgery is entitled, *"HETERODOXY, SERENDIPITY and research—How We Got Here,"* in which I relate the above anecdotes about the success of heretical modalities and the unexpected salvage of the heart tumor as pathways to innovation that are sometimes more valuable than research.

Nevertheless, I have spent many a long hour in the laboratory on a variety of projects the results of which are listed in the attached bibliography. Most of these reports are technical developments of minimal interest to the lay reader. One project, however, is worthy of comment. It came about rather curiously when a young man named Paul Davis came to my office soliciting my interest in testing an artificial heart he had designed and built. The quest for a satisfactory mechanical replacement for the heart was not new and the need was certainly pressing in a world where cardiac disease was the commonest cause of death, despite the great advances in surgical reconstruction and new cardiac medications. Cardiac transplantation was successful but it had its limitations and the supply of donors was way behind the demand.

Many devices had been built, both for external pumping and for implantation but all were and remain flawed on various counts. The obstacles to this objective are daunting and Davis had no clinical background, not even an engineering degree. He owned and operated a pipe factory but he was so eager, his pump was so well designed, and his objective so worthy that I hated to shut him off. Rather than reject his proposal summarily, I explained to him that a heart has to pump varying amounts according to differing circumstances and that I would be interested in his project if he could produce a pump that would eject each stroke what may be delivered to it over a range of zero to 60cc. I thanked him for his interest and said good-bye, never expecting to see him again.

Six weeks later, he returned with a pump that fulfilled my requirement and I was obliged to fulfill my promise despite the enormous challenge of funding, scheduling, equipping, and arranging for the project. Bud Smail was the surgical resident attached to the animal laboratory and he was of tremendous help in making it go. Davis' device was too large for the usual laboratory animal and we had to obtain two-month-old calves and develop suitable apparatus to anesthetize them and run them on a heart-lung machine. It was an enormous project that required facilities and personnel far exceeding our capabilities but we hoped that our initial efforts would provide enough basis to obtain a major grant to do the project properly. Paul Davis came over from Alameda for each operation, providing valuable assistance and equipment through laborious hours of frustration and failure. Finally however, we were rewarded with a calf that survived having its left ventricle completely defunctioned and its cardiac output maintained by the air driven pump. Three days later we devised a canvas saddle to carry a compressed air tank (to drive the pump) and took the calf out into a field where he was photographed trotting around free of any impediment and with its Davis Pump circulation sustaining the significant exercise. It was a major step in what might have been a successful project. Unfortunately, after eight days of being sustained on the artificial heart, the animal died of infection because our laboratory facilities were too crude to provide appropriate surgical sterility and it was impossible to prevent the large mechanical heart from contamination and inevitable sepsis.

This moment of triumph was, however, fleeting. Our tenuous achievement had been accomplished on a shoestring budget with primitive facilities. Appropriate further development and testing of this device required funding which I attempted to obtain from the NIH but was turned down and we ran out of money to continue. Although the design principles of Davis' device were better than anything else then under investigation, the NIH had already committed support to the ongoing major projects underway at the University of Utah and at Baylor in Houston. Much as I would have liked to see Paul Davis achieve his dream, however, it would not have been feasible to mount the kind of institutional support needed for this kind of endeavor. But it was fun trying.

CHAPTER 18

Infiltrating the Mogul's Lair

A century ago, the scope of human knowledge and expertise was limited to a dimension that made it possible for a bright, diligent and energetic individual to be the master of several fields. But today the term Renaissance Man is seldom used because the enormity of each field and the intensity of competition within that field make it virtually impossible to excel in even a narrow area without total devotion to a singular objective. Athletes train for endless hours meeting rigorous demands that press their limits; scholars toil at 100+ hour weeks and give up vacations; and numerous professional endeavors, such as cardiac surgery, are so demanding as to leave little time for family or leisure, let alone other pursuits. It is a paradox that my career has somehow been so variegated. Whether the level of achievement and national recognition in my chosen profession is notable is a matter of opinion, but the competition included the best and the brightest of my surgical generation and the recognition I enjoyed reflected at least modest success. That I was able further to enrich my good fortune by supplementing this academic and clinical endeavor with numerous other pursuits is surprising.

Surgical Politics

What later became an extensive involvement in national surgical politics evolved from minimally conscientious participation in various organizations and committees on which I was invited to serve for initially menial tasks. My decision to leave Boston and to sacrifice the sponsorship of mentors at the MGH would predictably eliminate any opportunity of attaining professional leadership. Nevertheless my instinctive and irrepressible urge to be involved in the political and educational processes led progressively to a series of positions at the inner circle of power. Looking back on the occasions, I recognize being an active and conscientious participant wherever I was involved but with no expectation of playing any of the important roles that eventually befell me. As everyone knows nearly all political appointments are guarded and jealously controlled by the entrenched senior establishment that picks its own successors to perpetuate its image and power. But our specialty was new and burgeoning, with mentors and leaders still young and in the process of becoming identified. While there was no dearth of bright competition, the specialty was expanding and open so it was possible for anyone to achieve some recognition by submitting and presenting innovative studies at national meetings where I met and exchanged ideas with my counterparts around the country. My introduction to the power elite, however, was purely by chance. The Board of Thoracic Surgery conducted its oral examinations at different venues and augmented its own small examining team of board members by recruiting recognized local practitioners as guest examiners. When the board visited the Bay Area on three occasions, I was tapped for this distinctive and important "chore" not because of any remarkable achievements but merely as one of the few local surgeons who had been certified by the recently instituted board. This role led to intimate relationships with the directors of the board during two days of intensive examining interspersed with pleasant socializing at conferences and meals. These men, my seniors by only a very few years, were the originators of the specialty and the beginning of what was to become its establishment. Friendship with them proved to be a valuable entrée when seeking help or advice in the early stages of chest and heart surgery. This information had to be obtained on a one-to-one basis because we had no textbooks and almost no established doctrine. As a natural consequence of those contacts I was later to be nominated and selected to serve on the board. That elite position led, in turn, to being appointed to the Residency Review Committee for Thoracic Surgery, and later to the American Board of Medical Specialties. Each of these appointments was an effective platform for my quest to improve standards.

Meanwhile, the long established national organization for this new and burgeoning specialty, the prestigious American Association for Thoracic Surgery (AATS), was unable to expand its restrictive membership to keep pace with the growing number of trained practitioners in the field. This discrepancy highlighted the need for more than one national organization for the specialty. That need was fulfilled by a small coalition who developed a new, less elite, and more encompassing organization for the certified journeyman practitioner in Thoracic Surgery, leaving the senior association as the goal for those productive individuals who had achieved distinction and leadership. This new society came about during the two years that I was Chairman of the AATS Membership Committee, which was consequently mandated to establish new criteria for membership. My committee chaperoned its metamorphosis from accepting applicants with almost any respectable identification in the field to establishing the criteria for recognition of scientific productivity and/or a leadership role.

The new organization was initiated and led by Buck Samson of Oakland who—as I described—had become my friend and mentor. I became a charter member of this new Society of Thoracic Surgeons (STS), participated in its first programs, and served on its committees. These activities were gratifying and afforded some degree of political influence, but I had no reason to expect attaining a major leadership role. However, at the Society's eighth meeting in Dallas I appeared at the president's reception, to which I was flattered to be invited, where I was casually told that my name would be nominated as the next president-elect. It was such a total surprise and unlikely occurrence that I assumed my leg was being pulled. The probable explanation was that Buck Samson had introduced my name as a compromise candidate to resolve a power struggle because I was certainly not what anyone would have considered to be a strong contender. But, deserved or not, it was a fortuitous and exciting moment that inserted my presence into the circle of influence.

It would have been a stimulating indulgence merely to revel in the glory of a presidency and accept the privilege of transient power without finding a need to use it for anything substantive. However, I utilized the unique opportunity provided by that office to initiate new programs and reforms in the standards and practices of our new and still wet behind the ears specialty. The time was ripe for amalgamating the explosive advances in technology with the emergence of the lengthy, structured surgical residency training programs. The specialty had just achieved independent identity by designation of the full-fledged American Board of Thoracic Surgery, from its previous status as a subordinated affiliate of the American Board of Surgery, so the policies and directions of the young specialty were in the process of being formulated. The future of the specialty was bright because its fascinating challenges had attracted many of the best trained and most innovative surgical talent of the post World War II generation. But its rapid growth and popularity created problems of assuring quality and fairness in the training programs and in clinical practices. My attempt to focus attention and to promote society action in these areas were outlined in my presidential address. With this presentation I had the rare privilege of commanding the full attention of the Society with no interruptions and few constraints on time or content. Under the title of "Whither in Maturity?"[xv] I recognized the recent and dramatic metamorphosis of our specialty from a minor aspect of general surgery to a major field of its own which had emerged to rival established specialties like Orthopedics, Ophthalmology and Neurosurgery. I challenged our leadership to undertake greater civic and professional responsibility in the training requirements, hospital practices and accountability of our profession. I was pleased that the proposals were well received and that the message was promptly acknowledged by the appointment of new committees in the Society to address the challenges. A genuine effort was launched to improve clinical performance, to gather data and to establish standards of practice.

Cardiac surgery could not develop in the obscurity of a remote laboratory. It was highly conspicuous and viciously competitive, with critics lurking behind every post. Because its success and failure is measured with life and death, not with merely annoying complications, performance deficiencies were not easily forgiven. Not surprisingly, there were pressures for accountability and I am pleased that we were able to make so much of it happen.

Presumably, because I was identified with that thrust I was appointed by the American College of Surgeons to chair its newly developed Advisory Council for Thoracic Surgery for three years. During that period, the specialty assumed new influence and importance among the older established surgical specialties.

By the end of my customary six year term on the board (ABTS) I had been passed over for the chairmanship, allegedly because of my contentious posture on policies and directions. However, I was asked to stay on for an additional year to complete my project of restructuring the examination process to improve its reliability and validity. At the end of that year there was an apparent change of heart and I was elected to be vice-chairman for a two year term as the stepping stone to becoming chairman in 1981. That event was the apex of my career, not just because of the honor it represented as the cardinal responsibility of our profession but more particularly because it provided, once again, the opportunity to influence the quality and integrity of the board's function.

Getting involved in professional politics had never been my ambition but when chance opportunities arose I found myself almost eager to be involved, to create innovations and to take on a leadership role for its opportunity to bring about reforms. This role became a major source of satisfaction and an important supplement to the pleasures I derived from technical surgery, research and teaching.

It has been gratifying to recognize some of the useful changes that have resulted from initiatives that I had the opportunity to introduce. Of course, these actions would have been little more than straws in the wind were it not for being accepted into a forum *within* the establishment. That recognition could only have been attained by at least a respectable degree of conformity. The process of reaching a position of power and influence, by someone of my non-political proclivities, is interesting, surprising, and perhaps simply dumb luck.

My ideas were supported and augmented by like-minded colleagues who were no longer throttled by the senior establishment in general surgery. We succeeded in initiating a few important measures to raise standards. With my urging, practice guidelines for cardiac surgery were developed, steered through political opposition, and published through the Cardiovascular Committee of the American College of Surgeons. And similar guidelines were later created for thoracic surgery through the ACS's Advisory Council for Thoracic Surgery when I was its chairman. The Residency Review Committee during my tenure expanded both the scope and volume of the surgical case experience required to qualify for approval of the program. Applicants who trained in mixed programs that provided variable and borderline experience were eliminated from eligibility for certification by persuading the Board of Thoracic Surgery to accept only candidates who had completed a separate cardiothoracic residency program that had been inspected and approved by the committee. This measure was offensive to the great institutions, such as the MGH and Johns Hopkins, who had produced the leaders in our field from their Residencies in general surgery and felt no need to develop a separate program in what they did not care to recognize as a separate specialty. It took a lot of persuasion to make these important institutions recognize that they had been able to train thoracic surgeons properly only because their general surgery programs were exceptional with abundant patient material and experienced teachers. In contrast were other general surgical programs which had deficient or borderline thoracic material and minimal professional guidance. Thus without being able to define a criterion for what level of material and teaching is adequate the Residency Review Committee opted for requiring a separate service for thoracic surgery with the expectation that no institution could afford to house and staff a new service that did not have a significant caseload and appropriate leadership.

In my presidential address I recommended creating a committee on standards and ethics, which was subsequently initiated by the society to provide adjudication and peer review in practice disputes. In my term as chairman of the Examination Committee of the American Board of Thoracic Surgery we laboriously improved the examination process by tightening and standardizing the test and hiring professional evaluators to verify its fairness and reliability. Each of these measures led to a substantial improvement in the quality and safety of cardiothoracic surgical practice in this country; and, since the U.S. led the world in this field, the repercussions were ultimately widespread. Consummating these policies and regulations took a considerable amount of time, effort, and guile, often with opposition from entrenched departments who sought to maintain their administrative prerogatives over thoracic surgery. It is human nature to resist change, particularly when established practices are threatened and when no obvious defect is forcing the issue. These efforts gained me a reputation as a boat rocker or troublemaker but I was fortunate to be surrounded by a large number of open-minded colleagues who eventually subscribed to these objectives. These endeavors yielded no remuneration and their success has either been taken for granted and forgotten or credited to others. But the end-product is the source of great satisfaction.

These achievements in quality assurance were easier to bring about in a new and complex field than it would have been to alter the deeply-rooted administration in the established specialties. Whatever the reason, the measures to raise standards were soon imitated by the other specialties. In order to avoid losing their accreditation, surgical residency programs everywhere became genuine educational experiences instead of the shams that many had made of them as a means to provide cheap professional labor. All specialty boards now require evidence that the applicant has received substantial operative experience—as the primary surgeon—across the full spectrum of procedures to qualify for taking the examination. Program directors were thus pressured to provide a well-rounded training. All Board examinations are now exhaustively dissected for fairness and reliability. And established standards of practice and performance now make it more feasible to face the difficult task of curtailing the practice of an incompetent or badly performing surgeon.

It is notable that the public has unknowingly derived great benefit from these quality standards, all of which were self imposed by our profession without any governmental regulation or licensing process. The death and suffering that has been averted by these selfless efforts is immeasurable. The benefits, of course, were two-way: (a) public safety was enhanced by disenfranchising the untrained would-be surgeons and (b) the qualified surgeons had their competition narrowed when hospitals limited operating privileges to those with board certification.

While these measures have materially reduced the public's exposure to the hazards of thoracic surgeons who are inadequately trained, bad practices have not been obliterated. The certification process cannot screen behavioral defects or technical incompetence. These aspects of performance are left to those responsible for hospital staff privileges. In general, there is a high degree of integrity in that process but political forces, procedural details, and legal constraints prove to be impediments when it comes to verifying dangerous practices and curtailing the operating privileges of a culprit. Hospital trustees have traditionally delegated matters of qualification and discipline to the medical staff thus deputizing the fox to guard the hen house and allowing hospital by-laws to be written primarily to protect the interests of the physician. Only recently have hospitals recognized their potential liability for bad practices of their staff. I have published and promoted efforts to rewrite the by-laws so as to reflect more responsibility to patients than to medical staffs by facilitating suspension of privileges and evaluation of results with computerized data[xvi]. Certainly an airline would not await a tedious evaluation process before taking a plane with a cracked wing out of service, but to restrain a dangerous surgeon from operating can take months or years of process—often involving prolonged litigation—while he continues to practice. Although these episodes are thought to be relatively rare, I suspect otherwise on the basis of my awareness of two instances in which an incompetent surgeon caused dozens of deaths and complications that took longer than a year to be recognized and documented by the hospital administration, and almost two more years of litigation before the hospital could legally have the surgeon's operating privileges curtailed.

Reprehensible though this seeming atrocity may be, it is, however, probable that no other profession or activity is conducted with a higher degree of self-imposed quality assurance and public protection. Perfect it isn't, but excellent it is.

CHAPTER 19

The American Board of Thoracic Surgery

Probably the most important, the most prestigious, the most productive, and the most demanding aspect of my professional life was my term on the American Board of Thoracic Surgery. This body, like the official certifying boards of other medical specialties, is a free-standing, self-perpetuating group whose members are nominated by five different national surgical societies[xvii], but the Board itself selects its members from the nominees. With the exception of a small stipend for the enormous task of secretary-treasurer, the directors are not paid and derive no benefits from their lengthy and arduous work besides a comfortable hotel room (in which there is barely time to sleep) and some pleasant meals with their colleagues. Terms are usually for six years but circumstances can cause an extension of that term.

The ultimate goal of the Board is to establish, to maintain and to improve the standards of care in the practice of cardiothoracic surgery. That is partially achieved through the process of determining the qualifications for being identified as a specialist and by screening candidates to verify that they have met those qualifications. If the quality and duration of their training is approved, they are subjected to a series of examinations to evaluate the candidates' knowledge. While there are no legal or licensing constraints on anyone who wishes to practice the specialty, it has gradually become an accepted criterion for obtaining hospital privileges, for specialty designation in government services, and for payment by some insurers. To undertake some complex and hazardous special procedures, such as brain surgery and heart surgery, without board certification would invite a malpractice action from the slightest mishap. Despite a lack of legal sanction it has become almost a misrepresentation to identify as a specialist *without* board certification.

As a new field that emerged into its own from successfully treating chest wounds in World War II, thoracic surgery had been a minor element of general surgical practice. Its first official identity as a specialty occurred in 1947 when the American Board of Surgery established a subsidiary Board of Thoracic Surgery. The founding members of that board were a distinguished group of pioneers in the field, nearly all of whom—at that time—had every reason to retain their identity as general surgeons because the field was new and there were not sufficient opportunities to warrant exclusive attention to it. But the field grew rapidly in that period and a cadre of young surgeons who did concentrate their practice in that field expanded quickly.

My first encounter with the board was as an examinee in 1953, when the embryonic training requirements and examination process were both fairly relaxed, when the early established practitioners of the specialty had no specific training, and when there was little or no consensus about either the criteria for passing, the protocol for questioning the candidates, or the content of the questions. I was examined in two unstructured oral sessions with paired teams consisting of a Board member and a local practitioner. There was no written examination. I was pleased to be passed but I had little feeling that the process had been comprehensive or incisive. It was, however, a well-intended process and a genuine effort to eliminate the incompetent and untrained applicant.

My second encounter, only a couple of years later, was as an invited guest examiner, which allowed me to become more closely acquainted with the imperfections and unfairness of the process. Candidates were subjected to the same procedure of two half hour oral examinations as I had experienced and I learned that the examiners used questions of their own making without either prior review or even consulting each other. They submitted separate grades, which were collated by the Secretary. At the conclusion of a long and exhausting day of examining 12 to 15 candidates, the whole examining team gathered around, while having cocktails, to hear a list of collated grades and to discuss the individual performances of those who had been given a failing or borderline grade by one team but not by the other. The purely subjective and arbitrary evaluations of this variegated group

inevitably involved cronyism and there were times when a personal endorsement by one of the examiners would prevail over a bad performance, often
with little or no verification. Nevertheless it must be acknowledged that the
laborious examination process was a step in the right direction toward
developing a screening mechanism that would provide some degree of quality assurance. Previously, the only testing in thoracic surgery had been as a
small fraction of the general surgery board examination, which was grossly
inadequate to screen for competence in the field.

For the next ten years or more, I served as an intermittent guest examiner and became well known to the members of the board. It was a task that
I enjoyed and a role that I had coveted. It was no great surprise but a great
satisfaction to be nominated by the American Association for Thoracic
Surgery and appointed to the board in 1971. Donald Paulson of Dallas was
chairman at that time and he welcomed innovation. Steps were initiated
under his leadership to shape the examination from a crude, inconsistent
and informal process into a valid and meaningful method of distinguishing
the qualified candidates from those who were inadequately trained. The
screening mechanism evolved progressively into two phases. The single
informal and totally unstructured oral examination was replaced by a two
phase process that began with a segmented written exercise encompassing
each of the four aspects of thoracic surgery (congenital cardiac, adult cardiac, pulmonary [lung], and mediastinal [central chest]), which occupied a
full day. The oral examination was given some months later and was
changed to four half-hour structured sessions of one-on-one examiner/can-
didate encounters. Passing grades were initially based on the combined
score of both written and oral examinations, which made it possible to offset a failure on one part by a good score on the other, thus potentially circumventing the objective of requiring adequate factual knowledge as well as
sound clinical judgment and problem solving. This defect in achieving our
objective bothered me more than it seemed to concern the others so I campaigned to establish a sequential procedure in which passing the written
exam became a precondition to taking the orals and was eventually successful in convincing the board to change its established format. Once it got
going they were all pleased with the results.

A lot of effort went into making the process fair and reliable. It
improved progressively through the arduous procedure of constructing, gathering, editing, discussing, and reviewing the questions in which the entire fif-

teen man board participated. This exercise represented thousands of highly skilled professional man hours, all without remuneration. Later, the board hired professional examiners to critique our process and our product as well as to provide mathematical analysis of our results. We were gratified to learn that our examination process was critically evaluated as being highly discriminating and statistically reliable. It was interesting, however, that despite our lengthy and meticulous review process to screen for flaws, there were always one or two questions on the examination that inexplicably proved to be invalid (simply because most of the high performers had failed it); these questions were then deleted from the exam grading as an ultimate act of fairness, even though the whole board had approved them as valid and clear.

Both the written and oral examinations were divided into subject categories and structured to encompass all aspects of the field. Each of four subject areas in the oral examination was covered by two separate examiners, both of whom were required to agree about an unsatisfactory performance before a candidate was given a failing grade in that sector. Initially, the pass-fail delineation was the product of numerically collating the separately submitted grades, which at first seemed reasonably fair. However, our post mortem discussions revealed that some examiners had harbored varying degrees of uncertainty about their ratings, whereas others were confident about their determinations, making it seem inappropriate to balance one against the other. I proposed, and the Board agreed, to address this problem by postponing the final grading until after a caucus following each two hour rotation in which all four examiners of that group of examinees sat down and reviewed in detail every evaluation that was inconsistent with the others. It was gratifying that there was fairly close agreement about most of the evaluations as a result of how the examination was structured. But whenever there was disagreement it was quickly and easily resolved by group consensus. Every examiner who had submitted a failing grade was obliged to defend it by describing to the caucus how he considered the candidate's answers to be unsatisfactory, after which they voted to validate or reject the failure. This procedure added another dimension to the fairness and significance of the examination.

The oral examination team of twenty-four men perforce consisted of several guest examiners who required some coaching to provide the desired service. The board commissioned me to develop a video tape on how to (and how not to) conduct an oral examination, which I produced on a shoestring budget, using our surgical residents as actors. It served as an instructional tool for examiners for many years after I left the board.

It was a great satisfaction to participate in and to influence the evolution of a meaningful process that was reliably discriminating and fair. Our procedure became a model that was eventually copied by virtually all the other certifying boards.

Although this experience required an enormous amount of time, effort and travel, it was richly rewarding by its intimate relationship with stimulating peers who represented the leadership of my burgeoning profession. The ultimate honor of serving as their chairman was a political challenge of the first order because each member of the Board was a king in his own domain and not always amenable to being led. Our meetings were lively and interesting by virtue of several colorful characters and strong-minded personalities. There were no tender egos to be mollycoddled and disagreements got resolved at full voice. It was a most enjoyable role, punctuated by delightful rapport with respected and interesting colleagues in fine restaurants and nice hotels.

The only part of the now well developed process with which I took issue was the determination of what over-all score would be the pass/fail line. Almost from the beginning of numerical grading the board had traditionally put the pass/fail point at the eightieth percentile on the Bell Grading Curve. It was my contention that allowing the performance of the examinees to be a determinant would sidestep the board's responsibility to establish its own standard of performance for qualification. The percentile method would preclude an appropriate response in the event that progressive improvement in the process of selection and training were to result in widespread excellence so that *few or none* of those well qualified products should properly be failed, but the system would necessarily cause twenty percent to be flunked. Or conversely, there could be a group of candidates, a large proportion of whom were poorly trained or incompetent and *most* of whom should properly fail, but eighty percent would automatically be passed with that system. I was not initially successful in selling my interpretation of the board's mission to be a public service which should determine and maintain an acceptable standard of competence in the specialty with a willingness to pass as many as all or as few as none. I was convinced that certification should represent meeting a standard that was determined by experienced experts and not influenced by how the candidates performed. This impropriety was raised by me several years in a row to no avail. But a resolution to correct it was finally passed at my final meeting of the board the year that my term ended. That resolution was later rescinded but now, at long last, is incorporated in the examination procedure so the board can say that it provides a meaningful standard by which to measure qualification and to which the training directors can lead their programs.

The Thoracic Surgery Directors Association

An important adjunct to the certifying board developed fortuitously in the form of an informal group composed of the service chiefs of thoracic surgery training programs that had met casually for several years at a breakfast bull session to air their problems and to complain about the obstacles created by the board and the Residency Review Committee. The importance of this group became more evident, and I helped Hassan Najafi of Chicago to evolve it into an effective body, called the Thoracic Surgery Directors Association that played an active and useful role, in close liaison with the board, to address the problems and issues of residency training. Naturally, I was pleased to be elected to the presidency of this rump organization because it provided a forum to address the board's problems and to clarify its frequently misunderstood objectives to the program chairmen, whose administrative and practice problems frequently had a higher priority than education.

The screening capabilities of the board are effectively limited to approval of a candidate's training credentials and to evaluating his factual knowledge and his thought processes in the examination process. Of perhaps even greater importance are the applicant's technical competence, sound clinical judgment and moral integrity, none of which the Board had any capability to ascertain. These elements had to be screened by the candidate's mentors.

It is true that the board requires the program director to endorse a candidate's qualification and to attest that he/she had demonstrated the aforementioned moral and intellectual qualities as a condition of accepting an applicant to take the examination. Certainly it should be expected that the director and faculty of the training program, with whom the candidate has worked on a daily basis for at least two years, are those best able to evaluate that individual's performance and behavior. Unfortunately, however, this process involves politics and personalities that frequently stand in the way of candid, objective reports. The program directors are in an awkward position to deal with an unsatisfactory trainee and are inclined to be generous with their evaluations, either from guilt over failing to dismiss an incompetent performance before its completion, or out of loyalty to a resident who has worked hard and been a useful, if flawed, pair of hands for the team.

My efforts to persuade the program directors not to dump the screening responsibility on the board but to shoulder the inconvenience and embarrassment of dropping an unsatisfactory resident in mid-course were of doubtful influence. My thrust was to put the monkey on the program director's back by declaring it to be a hoax, and perhaps even a libelous negligence, to be a party to the certification of one who could be a potentially dangerous surgeon but who just might have enough knowledge to pass the examination. In addition, I argued, it is a cruel disservice to lead someone along a path in which failure is probable instead of redirecting him/her as early as possible to a more suitable career.

The difficulty in persuading others to address this problem is that the residency training program is a source of manpower that has become integral to patient care; the resident staff plays a key and indispensable role in the function of teaching hospitals. Dropping a trainee in mid year would create a major logistical crisis and finding a replacement would be very difficult, if not impossible. There is a strong disincentive to taking drastic action in response to a poor performance or behavior. Better a defective helper than a void. Then at the terminus of a two-year intimate daily association, the program director faces a greater moral pressure to endorse his candidate and presumed protégé than to address the lack of moral responsibility for potential future misdeeds of an individual who will be long gone from the scene. By not providing honest and objective evaluations of trainees who are lacking in one or more of the non-cognitive qualities the program director does a serious disservice to both the board and to the consumer public who should be able to rely on the certification process to assure safe and reliable surgical performance. My plea was not successful in eliminating the problem but it did bring the issue into focus and evoked some recognition of long-term consequences. At least it was one more stone in the wall to build a strong and creditable process of training and certifying cardiothoracic surgeons. That we have failed to achieve perfection in this final link is regrettable but we have established a screening mechanism (certification) that is a far more reliable index of competence than what can be found in any other profession or trade.

There will be very few who will identify these improvements in the certifying process with my personal efforts because they were achieved gradually, even insidiously, and always in concert with others. Nor do I desire any recognition for them. But certainly those of our professional specialty, as a group, can be proud of its quality and integrity. Having contributed significantly to that accomplishment is the source of great personal satisfaction, for which I am grateful to the board as the principal instrument in achieving it.

At its fiftieth Anniversary, the board published a beautifully documented history,[xviii] compiled by Dr. Herbert Sloan, who was secretary-treasurer for thirteen years. I'm not sure whether to be proud or embarrassed that my name appeared in the book more times than any other's in a long roster of distinguished directors. Perhaps that occurred because of my extended service but many of the references were to the innovations I had suggested but that some had thought to be boat rocking. In any case, it was the pinnacle of my professional career not only to chair this important body but also to have played such a pivotal role in molding its performance and reputation as a fair and meaningful certifying body.

While recent press releases have revealed the deplorable fact that a number of patients continue to be harmed by careless or incompetent surgeons, including thoracic surgeons, that incidence has undoubtedly been drastically reduced by the training requirements and the incentives to become certified. Certainly the situation today is dramatically better than it was before widespread board certification when almost no surgeons had the training and experience now required of all surgeons even before taking the examination. Further steps to assure universal competence are still necessary but the certifying process has resulted in establishing a general performance of high quality, which other professions have only recently begun to match. I applaud the measures to expose negligent and/or incompetent professionals, but I regret that the public has not been made sufficiently aware of how much the general level of competence has been elevated and how open and conscientious the profession has been about addressing its problems.

CHAPTER 20

The Work-Play Conflict

E veryone—including even the very wealthy—lives with a conflict between a desire for personal pleasure and an urge to be useful or productive. Those with the means to indulge themselves limitlessly are usually driven by moral pressures or conscience to use their wealth responsibly and/or to demonstrate some kind of societal virtue. At the opposite end of the scale are those who must work even for life's simple necessities and are forced to find both their recreation and any sense of virtue outside the work-place. The truly fortunate are those who enjoy pleasure and satisfaction from an occupation that also happens to be financially rewarding or are those whose financial independence allows them to undertake a productive career as an avocation (as was true of many on the Harvard Medical School faculty). The truly *un*fortunate are those who detest their work and do not have enough free time or opportunity to balance it with pleasurable activity.

Regardless of one's category, however, the forces of indulgence are at odds with the need (or desire) to be productive. When one interferes with the other it forces a choice between the conflicting impulses. The balance, of course, is influenced by habits and training. Those imbued with the "Puritan Ethic", which was prevalent in New England, are programmed toward the drive to work and those addicted to self indulgence are inclined to play.

In my own case a competitive drive and a strong element of ambition were variably counterbalanced by an insidious sybaritic impulse. The exact extent to which that weakness impaired my professional success can only be guessed, but certainly it was a threatening factor, that by all rights should have been my undoing. I certainly did not work as diligently as I could have either in college or in medical school simply because I was not sufficiently conscientious or disciplined to eschew the social and recreational temptations that crossed my path. It was evident that most—if not all—of my successful colleagues at any level were dedicated to putting more time and energy into their studies or their research or their professional duties than I managed to do, so I could never begrudge their superior performance. I knew full well that this reluctance to make a total commitment in a highly competitive milieu was a dangerous gamble—even as the drug addict or alcoholic recognizes the folly of his indulgence and its threat to his success as he pours his next drink. It obviously came close to doing so in my senior year on the crew and many has been the final examination in which I regretted not studying just a little bit more. Certainly by the accepted standards of Horatio Alger's virtue and behavior I should never have been allowed the coveted labels that somehow appear on my credentials, not only because of short changed dedication but also because of my unpopular inclination to speak out against conventional thought whenever I indulged the arrogance of considering the convention to be unreasonable.

My weakness for self indulgence in medical school can be attributed the very genial and pleasant ambiance of the Vanderbilt Hall Dormitory and its multiple social opportunities which are described in Chapter 6. Enjoyment was difficult to eschew in the company of such bright and interesting colleagues. It is no wonder that I had some apprehension about my academic standing but—as I mentioned earlier—we were ignorant about our grades and only assumed we had squeaked by if the ax didn't fall. This weakness did much to prevent my life from being dull and added a multitude of pleasures for which I am grateful—even at the expense of a guilty conscience.

Later in life when I should have devoted maximum energy toward advancing my career I stole time off to play squash and tennis, I bought a boat and took up sailing with a vengeance, I joined a duck club and hunted regularly, and I enjoyed an active social life. But just as I succumbed to the temptations of recreation I also was a patsy for nearly every invitation to serve on boards and committees as attested in my C-V. (Appendix B) These activities consumed a lot of time and effort while providing satisfaction about doing some civic and professional service.

Lest the reader infer that these paradoxes represent an extraordinary talent for effortless competition I should point out that *none* of my mentors, leaders, coaches, teachers or advisors have ever expressed any superlatives about my performance. Yes, the MGH expected it of us and the crew coach seemed to think I needed humbling but there were many other endeavors that could have been complimented. Yes, I did make the grade to attain a long list of credentials, but always with some hesitation or uncertainty—always on the fringe. My family has often tried to persuade me not to attribute my success to good fortune but my persistence with this posture derives from a keen awareness of so many brighter, more diligent and more worthy competitors who have not shared my satisfactions and are far less comfortable with their surroundings than I am. Students of probability will say that luck balances out in the long run and that disproportionate winning must reflect an element of skill. Perhaps so, but only occasionally have I been able to recognized some truly meritorious advantage over my peers and I cannot dispel the feeling that I have been exceptionally lucky in love, work and war.

Neither, however, should it be inferred that every step of my career has been without trauma or disappointment. Indeed there have been many important occasions on which I paid a heavy price for my outspoken posture or for espousing an unpopular position That, of course, is the crucial paradox of my story. On each of the several times when I was rejected or excluded from a coveted or seemingly deserved identity it was associated with some contrary posture or less than dedicated behavior that was anathema to one or more influential individuals who were in a position to block my progress. The "top of the mountain" in our specialty is the presidency of the American Association for Thoracic Surgery for which my roles had made me a more than likely contender but I never made it, for speculative reasons of being too radical. I must confess coveting this honor but I thoroughly understand the limitations of riding both sides of the fence.

None of this scenario was deliberately undertaken with a sense of martyrdom or courage but it just evolved because I was less impelled by a political objective than by impetuous expression—even in politically sensitive situations. With the benefit of retrospect it is easy to demonstrate where tactful hypocrisy—or even silence—would have been greatly to my advantage. But that is just not in my nature and thus I am obliged to be thankful that the consequences have not been completely disastrous. By some quirk of fate or circumstance I was able to wear two hats, that of the conventional and conservative in one breath and that of the heretic and rebel in the next. Why it didn't get me thrown out of both camps is amazing but, of course, it kept me on the fringe of acceptance and naturally prevented acclamation by either faction. Challenging orthodoxy is a dangerous undertaking and getting away with it has been unlikely fun.

And what a privilege it has been to enjoy my work. No pleasure has been greater than standing at the operating table dealing with a complex problem within the heart.

CHAPTER 21

Political Disaster

The course of events during my tenure as Chief of Cardiothoracic Surgery at UCSF was very gratifying in its teaching and research aspects and reasonably satisfying in its clinical and academic aspects within the limits imposed on my opportunities but politically it was a disaster. On reviewing the sequence of events it is astonishing that I survived as long as I did so the reader should resist any temptation toward sympathy. Anyone who deliberately walks into a buzz saw and merely gets his shirt torn off is just plain lucky.

The durability and success of any leadership role is obviously dependent on the security of the position—the power and ability to keep at bay the inevitable detractors and competitors. I was acutely conscious of this truism from the first day I set foot in UC's Department of Surgery. Academic politics—which might be expected to operate on a high level of integrity and intellectual honesty—prove to be vicious and unscrupulous. It must be admitted that I was warned about UC's reputation before leaving Boston so I have no one to blame but myself for going back on my original decision to eschew academic sponsorship in the familiar milieu of the MGH. Hoping that the tempting and exciting initiative of developing cardiac surgery in a different setting would somehow acquire the right trappings was naïve. Although this wishful thinking proved to be a mistake, when all is said and done I cannot truthfully say that the endeavor wasn't successful, nor that it wasn't worth the effort. It is natural to make comparisons with those who had optimal support and total control of their projects but those comparisons are specious.

When J. Englebert Dunphy, a fellow Harvard transplant 10 years my senior, was appointed to be our new Surgical Department Chairman in 1968 I was mistakenly hopeful that better days were ahead. He hit the Department like a storm and quickly strengthened it with a new spirit for which he was immensely popular. He got the rest of the Surgical Department to do the Morbidity/Mortality review, which I had introduced on my service, and he greatly improved the candor in Grand Rounds discussion with his clever wit and effective leadership. He did all the things I would have done as the Department Chairman and I was initially delighted to welcome a bright new era that reminded me of my MGH days and kindled great expectations.

Thus it was a huge disappointment to discover that my problems were not part of his agenda. On the surface he was very friendly and seemingly supportive so I found it difficult to understand his behavior on several scores: He found excuses not to back my position in various administrative and interdepartmental disputes about patient referrals and post operative management, thus publicizing my political impotence. He introduced onto my service—without my knowledge or approval—one of his protégés from Boston, whose declared objective was to establish a separate service and who considered himself accountable to Dunphy and not to me. He appointed—without my consultation or approval—a Chief of Cardiothoracic Surgery at the Veterans Hospital, which was part of my training program but over which I was allowed no influence. And most devastating was Dunphy's "State of the Union" report to the faculty at the end of his first year in office, in which he expressed strong and optimistic expectations for each of the various sectors of his Department with one notable exception. He ended the list with a casual diminuendo comment that "we would have a modest cardiac surgical program which would not try to compete with Frank Gerbode (Stanford)". Thus he publicly acknowledged that my position was insignificant and would not be strengthened. And later he displaced me from my space in the animal laboratory to provide for his local protégé, Larry Way, thus curtailing my scientific productivity.

Each of these actions might have had some reasonable explanation that I did not appreciate but collectively they were devastating to my progress and couldn't help provoking paranoia. It was not until after his death that the reason was revealed. Bert's previous role as Chairman at the University of Oregon had an awkward aspect by virtue of the great success achieved by Albert Starr, the cardiac surgeon in his department. Starr developed a cardiac surgery unit with a world renowned reputation that far outshone the rest of the department. After Dunphy's death his great friend, Carleton Mathewson (at Stanford) told me that Bert had confided to him a determination not to let the same thing happen at UCSF. This information permits me to assume that his actions were not malicious but instead that he rationalized it was in the best over all interests of his Department to prevent Cardiothoracic surgery from becoming a dominant or even influential force. That interpretation fits Bert Dunphy's character whose admirable virtue was the effective leadership of a witty Irish politician who played the role of "Big Daddy" and kept the members of his team effectively subordinated. He sensed that I would be difficult to throttle if allowed to reach a strong position. I like to think he was right.

During this period—and indeed from the beginning of my attempts to develop Cardiothoracic surgery—our service held weekly open meetings for candid and intensive review of all deaths and complications as described above; a custom which I had brought from the MGH and (mistakenly) assumed to be standard practice. (My inquiry about why UC did not use this process when I arrived was met with a straight faced reply that "it was unnecessary because our faculty doesn't make mistakes.") Our conferences were also attended by the anesthetists, O.R. nurses and I.C.U. nurses. Referring cardiologists were invited in the hope that they would provide constructive criticism and recognize the quality of our work but they seldom appeared. It was naïve to believe that the truth would eventually prevail and disillusioning to learn that our candor instead became the source for deprecating gossip. But at least our efforts resulted in shortening the learning curve and improving results as well as providing a useful forum for creating and evaluating new ideas. We were thus able to achieve national recognition with a series of significant scientific presentations of these innovations either at national meetings or in major journals. More about these contributions later. Our training program was awarded a training grant from the National Institutes of Health and our service was repeatedly voted their favorite rotation by the surgical resident staff.

I had noted that many if not all of the strong cardiac surgical units around the country had autonomous or semi autonomous leadership which had broken out of the yoke of the Department of Surgery to have its own representation and participation in administrative matters such as those described above, which had been preempted by Dr. Dunphy. It was clear that my ability to function effectively was handicapped by having my interests dependent on Dunphy's whim. To address this obvious need I drafted a petition to the Dean for a semi autonomous Division—carefully following University Regulations—based on comparisons with existing Departments and Divisions at UCSF on matters of case load, teaching function, research productivity, national recognition, and also on the precedent of other institutions nationally, including the other (then 3) U.C. medical schools. By every one of these criteria our Service was eminently qualified for independent status. Unfortunately, however, the process required the approval of the Surgical Chairman before the Dean would act on it and Dunphy refused to endorse it. When I asked why, his response was simply, "I don't want it."

Despite these impediments to my authority and effective control of my supposed domain we continued to make the most of our restricted clinical opportunities with gratifying results and innovative research that were reported at national meetings. I developed—along with engineer David Moore—a prosthetic heart valve, compression molded from silicone rubber, that was successfully implanted in dogs and was one of the first successful human implantations. I also devised and used several new instruments and techniques for cardiac surgery. Paradoxically our achievements gained a reputation that was far brighter extramurally than it was intramurally.

But the real poison arrow evolved in the appointment of a new Chief of Pediatric Cardiology, Abraham Rudolph, who had achieved success and fame as a pioneer of cardiac catheterization in infants, thus opening the diagnostic door for cardiac surgery in the newborn. He was an enormously valuable addition to our faculty and a potential boon to my program but it is curious that his selection and recruitment was done without my participation as Chief of Cardiothoracic Surgery. Abe was raised and trained in South Africa where he may have been the victim of ethnic repression, which perhaps accounts for his ruthless behavior. He reveled in his power and exercised tight autocratic control over his staff and the clinical program in Pediatric Cardiology, which was the antithesis of what I was able to do. He quickly disposed of the faithful ladies who had maintained that service over the years (Olney and Simpson) and somehow determined that I was not to his liking. Despite my intense overtures to support his objectives he quickly embarked on a campaign to destroy my reputation with invidious rumors about every glitch in surgical outcomes and by sending patients elsewhere for their surgery or even by referrals to my subordinates. My ambitions and expectations and, indeed, my clinical career were destroyed by his actions. I shall never forget one occasion in Bert Dunphy's office when Rudolph had complained about a surgical complication of one of my patients to Bert—instead of to me—and I was called in to respond. While I was explaining the events I caught a flash of Rudolph's facial expression that displayed the most consummate hatred that I had ever seen. No explanation for this hostility has ever emerged and it is clear that I somehow failed to provide an appropriate behavior to suit his personality. I have no idea how that could have been achieved other than changing my image, and yielding to his every desire. We had clashed over his attempt to take over postoperative management and I had resisted his effort to have a "designated" *pediatric* cardiac surgeon at a time when we were still struggling to identify the whole Cardiothoracic specialty. But Abe was a very determined man and I was seen to be in his way.

His presumed reason for pursuing my removal, of course, was that his personal assessment of my skills, experience and performance was beneath his objectives for pediatric cardiology. Yet he had never watched me operate and refused to provide data or objective evidence to substantiate his complaint; he ignored my repeated invitations to participate in our weekly performance reviews; he failed to offer any constructive criticism whatsoever; and he refused to acknowledge my reports on the very satisfactory results with the few opportunities to operate on infant cardiac lesions that had come my way. Interestingly his chief criticism of me was that I had comparatively little experience with complex congenital anomalies, which was the direct result of his own doing; these patients, who were under his control, were being diverted away from my practice, thus preventing me from developing the very experience that he considered to be important.

It is embarrassing to acknowledge my naiveté about the magnitude of his perfidy and the futility of my efforts to achieve a strong and effective service. He was determined not to cooperate with me and he had persuaded both Dunphy and the Dean not to support my position. Of course it occurred to me that I may have failed to recognize some justification for his position so when Dean Krevans got us together to discuss the issue I made an offer that I thought he couldn't refuse. I laid it on the table that Rudoph was unmistakably seeking to remove me so I proposed a mechanism that could achieve that objective with a degree of respectability. I offered to submit a predated letter of resignation to the Dean for him to exercise on two conditions: (1) that Rudolph would suspend his vitriolic campaign of destruction and support my program with clinical opportunities and cooperation for a six month probationary period, and (2) that any time during or after that period my performance would be evaluated—by a surgical peer of *his* choice—and was found to be below that of the leading cardiac surgeons who might be candidates to replace me. Without hesitation he refused my proposal and would offer no explanation. And the Dean didn't blink. I knew then that my fate at UCSF had been sealed by the political clout of one powerful individual who had manipulated my superiors into displacing me. UCSF had no room for a Maverick.

Of course it was foolhardy to walk away with my tail between my legs and not document that proposal in writing with copies to the Chancellor and the Department Chairmen to flush out a justification for this political assassination. Instead I merely became indignant and frustrated about the vicissitudes of academic politics and was deeply disappointed to have my career aborted before its encouraging potential had been fully achieved. But naught is gained by self pity or by dwelling on issues of fairness. Indeed it could be argued that most of my accomplishments had been achieved at the unfair advantage of fortuitous timing and locale, so better I should be pleased and grateful for what *was* done and make the most of it. The alternative of registering a formal complaint for an Academic Senate adjudication was silly, probably futile, and even if victorious would certainly have been Pyhrrhic.

Just how Rudolph manipulated the disenfranchisement of my position without any semblance of a formal complaint or evaluation is unknown, except that he was very close to Dean Krevans, who had recruited him. Dunphy asked me to step down as Chief of the Service, which he did with no explanation other than my inability to "get along" with Rudolph. A committee was appointed to seek and recommend applicants for that post while I continued to run the service as if nothing had happened. Then when Bert Dunphy's retirement became imminent the issue was postponed for the participation of his successor. Abe managed to get appointed to the Search Committee for the new Surgical Chairman and manipulated the selection of Paul Ebert who was well established as a Pediatric Cardiac Surgeon with experience derived at Duke under David Sabiston and subsequently as Chairman of Surgery at Cornell in New York City. Thus I became neatly displaced from my leadership role to remain in place and rot on the vine.

Naturally my thoughts again turned back to my fateful decision to leave Boston and return to San Francisco. Would I have had comparable opportunities in Boston? Probably not. Did I realize that UC politics were messy? Yes, Dr. Churchill had warned me to avoid UC in favor of Stanford. Should I have expected hostility? Yes, I was a conspicuous misfit from day one despite every effort to overcome it. In the final reckoning was my endeavor a failure? Certainly not; a lot was accomplished; and considering the limitations the results were gratifying. We had put UC on the Cardiothoracic map and achieved significant national recognition in spite of the impediments. It is fun to fantasize about how much further we would have progressed with the kind of backing and opportunity that our more successful competition had enjoyed, but that's the stuff that dreams are made of.

It troubles me that this scenario has such a paranoid character. I have tried to be accurate about the facts and I fully recognize that how people react to me is of my own making. Perhaps I didn't deserve the outcome; but some might say that I didn't deserve the opportunity in the first place.

The tenure system has a lot of shortcomings, which I have often criticized, but it certainly played an important role for me. In the real world my situation would have simply been "out on the street", which might have been a good stimulus to start over in another location. But at the age of 60 it was an unattractive choice when it seemed appropriate to savor the benefits of what had been built so laboriously. Thus I allowed myself to believe the new Chief whose seemingly cordial overtures clearly indicated that I would continue to play a significant role and that my practice would be maintained. To the contrary, however, I was disappointed to learn that my referral patterns were being deliberately intercepted by his office and that my image was rapidly deteriorating as the result of a prevalent inference that Ebert's appointment had been primarily to remedy my alleged incompetence. There is no way to respond to that situation because there had been no objective evaluation to refute the allegations. Obviously I had lost a public relations contest and was in the situation of a politician voted out of office, worthy or not.

It came down to a choice between sulk, slink, or swallow. I could feel sorry for myself as a hapless victim of ruthless politics, or I could crawl away to another venue, or I could swallow my pride and make the most of a sad situation. The first was nonsense and the prospect of starting over at my age was dismal, particularly in the face of my proven ineptitude in bureaucratic politics. So I chose the latter, which was economically feasible thanks to my academic tenure. It was convenient to rationalize that I had done *most* of what I had set out to do and that I could enjoy the opportunities of a less demanding schedule.

Certainly I was resentful and depressed for a while and was persuaded to seek help from my psychiatrist friend, Harrison Sadler. He was a sensible and pragmatic person who soon threw up his hands after listening to my philosophical posture. I simply recognized that I had been put in a losing situation beyond my control, that I had voluntarily rescinded my initial decision to eschew academia, and that I had enjoyed 17 years of unexpected excitement and satisfaction. And I could manage to get on with my life. After all I had long recognized that cardiac surgery was not for the tender hearted.

This seeming disaster at what should have been the crest of my career actually turned out to have benefits that partially offset its frustrations and disappointments. Fortuitously I was provoked into other areas of interest and satisfaction that had been precluded by the burdens of clinical and research responsibilities. Thus the last chapter in my career took on a new dimension that otherwise would probably never have occurred. I became involved in leading travel groups of Cardiothoracic surgeons for the *People-to-People Citizen Ambassador Program*. I spent more time teaching residents and medical students. I took a 6 month sabbatical leave at the National Heart Hospital with the widely respected Donald Ross and the adjacent Cardiovascular Research Institute in London. We found a flat on Devonshire Street close to the hospital and indulged generously in the many virtues of that great city. We played tennis for 50 pence in nearby Regent Park, frequented the theater and various museums, and spent every weekend driving to different parts of England and Wales.

Participating in the surgical procedures, the clinical rounds and the research conferences was moderately interesting and edifying, particularly in reference to my long standing concern with valve surgery and replacement, which was Mr. Ross' major project. The process of obtaining a temporary license to operate entailed an amusing encounter with British bureaucracy. My *first* visit to the Medical Licensing Office resulted only in learning that I had to submit my medical school diploma. My *second* visit was armed with a certified affirmation from the Dean's Office at Harvard but that was deemed to be inadequate; only the original diploma would do. After conveying complex instructions to locate, dismount and ship the diploma I returned for my *third* visit, only to have it noted that the inscription was in Latin and required a translation. That accomplished (with a little fudging) I returned for a *fourth* visit finally to obtain the necessary license. However, the process was delayed for several minutes while the clerk disappeared into the archives to ascertain whether Harvard was on the approved list!

I was generously afforded an office and the partial use of a secretary at the Institute, which facilitated organizing, soliciting contributors and writing a surgical textbook, which occupied most of my afternoons following mornings in the operating room. It was an interesting interlude during which we made new friends and gained a perspective on British surgery, research and practice. But its function was primarily to get away from the shambles of changed attitudes on the Service which I had built and had been my pride and joy. Candor and self examination were replaced with imagery and political serenity. Rudolph was pleased and pediatric cardiac surgery thrived to punctuate what I had failed to do.

On returning to San Francisco I was sent to work at the Veteran's Hospital where it was a pleasure to teach the thoracic surgical resident, who started his two year appointment at that institution. The slower pace of that service and the relatively little time required of my dwindled practice permitted the opportunity to write—among other things to finish the book I had started in London [xix]. And I resurrected my interest in playing tennis on a regular basis. Coincidentally my earlier occasional experience as an expert witness in malpractice litigation rapidly expanded into a major activity. I had the time and energy to write on controversial subjects such as quality control, the drug war fraud, euthanasia and medical ethics. I wrote a *History of Cardiothoracic Surgery at UCSF* to document the events described herein but it was never published and remains buried in the Archives because its bitter story is no tribute to UC's academic politics. And then I began writing this autobiography.

CHAPTER 22

Travels With Slides

Provincialism haunts all of us in some degree. Comfortable associations with familiar faces and places provoke many people to be uncomfortable with others. This fear or discomfort is strongest where economic or geographic circumstances restrict exposure to outsiders and hence was prevalent in early civilizations where travel was difficult and expensive. In today's world, where planes carry more people from San Francisco just to New York every *day* than trains carried from San Francisco to all points east in a *month* before World War II, we have become much more cosmopolitan and a large portion of the population is familiar with a variety of cities and places around the world. Nevertheless, our fundamental provinciality is reflected in a tendency to bring isolationism in our baggage. As a society we tend to patronize hotels and restaurants that reproduce American ambiance and fare. We spend more time looking at museums and cathedrals than in making an effort to speak the language or in learning the thoughts and habits of the local people, thus missing the quintessential virtue of travel.

Retrospectively, I recognize that one of the most valuable fringe benefits of academia and professional recognition has been its adding that important dimension to travel. We have visited some forty-seven countries and scores of cities in the U.S., in most of which I have had some professional function, resulting in introductions and social activities with colleagues and counterparts in that locale. In every instance, we had close rapport with the local surgeons and teachers and in many places their hospitality extended into their homes and/or their private clubs. These exposures often resulted in long-term friendships and reciprocal encounters at our home all of which provided insight into their values, their attitudes, their politics and their problems, none of which could have occurred had we been ordinary tourists. The pleasures and satisfactions of belonging to this academic fraternity are immeasurable and probably are largely unappreciated.

In 1967 we toured South America informally but with the benefit of some speaking invitations and introductions that brought us into the private lives of surgeons in Lima, Buenos Aires, Sao Paulo and Rio de Janeiro. In Santiago, we happened to coincide with a visit by the illustrious and flamboyant Dwight Harken, of cardiac surgical pioneering fame at Boston's Peter Bent Brigham Hospital, and his delightful wife, Ann. We were both speakers at a session of the Chilean Society of Cardiology (that bestowed honorary membership on both of us) on the day that the world press announced the first human heart transplant by Christiaan Barnard in Capetown. That event resulted in our being besieged with questions about the significance and projected outcome of this headline event. It was fun opining about the surgical feat versus the challenge of tissue rejection, which was the predictable obstacle to long-term success. Thanks to the Harken's presence we were treated like royalty and had a delightful visit.

Even in later years when our travels have had only a recreational purpose we have sought out or stumbled onto previous contacts that resulted in delightful social occasions that often turned out to be the highlight of the trip. That occurrence was exemplified recently when we took a cruise along the east coast of Australia, ending up in Sydney. D'Arcey Sutherland, one of my surgical colleagues from Adelaide, Australia suggested that I write to Professor Rowan Nicks, who was the dean and pioneer of Australian cardiac surgery, for some travel suggestions. I sent him a formal and respectful letter inviting him to dinner on the evening of our arrival. The reply I received was surprisingly addressed to "Dear Ben," in which he adamantly declared his role of host and reminded me that he had visited my service and watched me operate for several days back in the early '60s and that we had invited him to dinner at our home. I was embarrassed not to have remembered his visit and immediately responded. The consequence of that exchange made our visit to Sydney memorable. He personally guided our tour and gave a charming dinner party in his home, which he cooked himself for a party of ten friends. We were also entertained by Dr. & Mrs. Allan Sharpe, who had shared our role as protégés of Sir James Learmonth in Edinburgh. They invited us to their lovely home, took us to an elegant luncheon at their golf club and drove us on an extended tour of the city. During our stay in Sydney we resided at The Australian Club (which reciprocated with my club in San Francisco) where a charming couple introduced themselves and invited us to visit them on our drive to Melbourne. They lived on a large farm in the country outside of Canberra, where we stopped to see the capitol. In Melbourne we saw Dr. and Mrs. Larry Simpson who had been on a tour with us in Europe. They invited us to dinner in their attractive home and took us to a fascinating game of Australian football. We left that vast country with a warm sense of their hospitality.

Among our various travels were thee interesting People-to-People trips with fellow cardiothoracic surgeons behind what was then the Iron Curtain. On two of those expeditions I was invited to lead the group, which meant that I could choose the invitation list, influence the itinerary, and communicate directly with the principals in each city. These were fascinating encounters that often required considerable leadership effort on my part and counseling on Jane's part, but which were the basis of close professional and social exchanges with our counterparts in the Eastern Block nations. The People-to-People organization provided excellent official and professional contacts to enhance our visits, but there were several occasions on which we were greeted by a surgical colleague whom I or one of our party had befriended at one of the scientific meetings in the US. One of those professional contacts, with whom I had dined in Chicago, turned out also to be an influential Hungarian functionary who provided a pleasant surprise for our arrival in Budapest. Our plane was unloaded out on the tarmac where a special bus brought just our party into a separate entrance at the airport to meet my friend and a couple of his colleagues in a private lounge with coffee and snacks. Our passports were gathered and while we socialized our entries were cleared and our baggage loaded on a bus without going through customs. It was a touch of elegance that impressed my constituents and was greatly appreciated.

My task of developing a program of talks at each venue involved assessing the level of sophistication of the audience and how well they would understand our English, sorting out the lecturing talent in our group, assuaging the egos of the untalented, and testing the limits of how far we could exceed the boundaries of conventional thought. We found that physicians everywhere were most receptive to controversial ideas. Most surprising was a tour of the People's Republic of China in the middle '80s where the hunger for knowledge and information was prodigious and the open-mindedness impressive. Our most dramatic encounter was in Shanghai, where we gave four talks to a seminar of some forty staff of all the cardiac surgical units in the area on subjects of innovation and change in the field. At the conclusion I commented that three of the four subjects had been surgical heresy less than ten years previously, the moral of which was that we must never blindly believe what we are taught because it may prove to be wrong. In the setting of an authoritarian society it was indiscreet of me to say it, but the young residents in the back of the room were visibly pleased and I could not assess the reaction of the stoic professors in the front row. That was per-haps pushing the prerogative of a visitor and I thought no more of it. Two nights later, a large banquet was held in a hotel with all the staffs— faculty, residents, nurses, technicians, etc.—and the usual toasts of international good will were exchanged. But the startling surprise was a salute from the senior professor who added to his polite greeting, "—and to Professor Roe we have a special thanks, for encouraging us to chal-lenge conventional teaching." Such a statement from a venerated senior surgeon in a totalitarian society was mind boggling. It reinforced my conviction that the Chinese are destined to dominate twenty-first Century civilization, not with atomic weaponry, but with sheer diligence and ingenuity, coupled with an eagerness to learn.

Among our impressive encounters was a visit to an operating theater in Shanghai where the ambiance was pitifully run down, paint peeling off the walls and ceiling, but in contrast to those shabby trappings was a sur-geon replacing an aortic valve in a patient's heart. It was a procedure with which I was intimately familiar and which dazzled me with its simplicity. There were only seven instruments on the table where I would have had about 200; there was only one assistant where I would have had two. The heart-lung machine looked familiar but when I commented that it looked like a *Sarns* Pump to the anesthetist who was running it, he replied that it was but that they had built it. Clearly what they lacked in expensive and sophisticated equipment was made up for by ingenuity and determination.

Everywhere we went in China the hospitality was gracious and friendly. People were open about their problems and limitations, and we were not conscious of authoritarian restriction. Their eagerness to learn how and why American surgeons do things was amazing. They were so persistent that during the intermission of our lectures I was followed into the men's room by a half dozen young residents who kept firing questions at me while I was standing at the urinal.

In contrast, was a subsequent brief encounter at a hospital in Tokyo, where I expected a supposedly democratic society to be open-minded. Instead, I heard a potentially controversial case presented but no one dared to speak until the Professor's opinion had been established. Despite obvious cause for dispute, no one expressed anything except to echo the leader. When I exercised my prerogative as a guest and politely differed I was astonished to recognize a palpable discomfort in the room. In Japan one must not challenge what one is taught.

In Russia, however, it was difficult to get an opinion out of anybody. They were polite and receptive to our lectures but said very little about their work or their results. There were endless excuses for not showing us their facilities. In Ukraine and Belarus, our colleagues were more open. And in Lithuania, there was a powerful spirit of defiance toward Russians.

Our underlying attitude of American superiority in cardiac surgery was chastened in more than one visit. We encountered a high caliber of surgery and research in Vienna under the guidance of Ernst Wolner, and similarly in Prague. Our most impressive encounter was on an unlikely detour in Spain to the small town of Santander on the north coast, where my friend Carlos Duran provided us with a remarkable show. A veritable spectrum of valve disease was presented by members of his staff, each doing a different procedure on the mitral valve in four operating rooms simultaneously. In the afternoon we heard presentations of sophisticated research projects underway in Carlos's surgical laboratories. The members of my group had been skeptical about diverting our itinerary to an unknown venue, but they came away more impressed than by anything else we had seen in Europe. Of incidental interest is the fact that Dr. Duran has subsequently had a brilliant career with international recognition of his work on valve repair and now resides in Montana where he runs a successful cardiac surgical clinic.

We returned from these enjoyable trips with a vastly expanded perspective of people, cultures, geography, and surgical skills.

CHAPTER 23

Dueling With Trial Lawyers

One of the most invidious aspects of medical practice is the seemingly inevitable ordeal of a malpractice lawsuit, with its embarrassing implications of irresponsibility and misbehavior, its burdensome imposition on a physician's time and attention, and its potential of financial disaster. Fortunately my experience with this ogre from a personal standpoint is limited to a single action in which a devoted patient of mine became paralyzed following a re-operation for aortic coarctation and sued the university as my employer. Although technically I was not the defendant, it was my actions and my reputation that was on the line and it was I who was subjected to the courtroom discomforts of degrading interrogation. The jury awarded the patient a million dollars on the basis of insufficient informed consent and later told me that they felt I had done no wrong but that the patient needed and deserved compensation. It taught me to be exceedingly careful and to pay careful attention to the feelings and needs of my patients. I was fortunate to avoid any other claims during 38 years of practicing a specialty fraught with complications and high mortality. I had learned the price of being sued and had subscribed to the moral obligation of all physicians to stand collectively against plaintiffs attorneys who were considered to be malicious enemies.

Such a posture must, of course, be predicated on the premise that all physicians are flawless in the execution of their clinical responsibilities and completely conscientious in their conduct. The reality of human behavior belies that assumption and it turns out that some physicians do cause serious harm to their patients because of carelessness, laziness or avarice. If we are to be a responsible profession we must do our best to protect our patients from unnecessary harm. We—and I more than most—have diligently sought to improve our standards of training and certification to provide the public with specialists who are well-trained, proficient and reliable. Our profession has a credible record in pursuing that goal.

That achievement, however, does not atone for the harm done by a few bad actors in our midst, whose behavior the profession has neglected to curtail and discipline. That role is more difficult and awkward to exercise. Efforts to get the American College of Surgeons involved in the house cleaning and disciplinary processes have been in vain. This attitude is undoubtedly related to the well-known fact that reluctant measures by a hospital to restrict a physician's practice have often elicited a retaliatory lawsuit. The deplorable result of this situation is that the tort system has been brought into play with all of its expensive and ugly consequences instead of the desirable alternative of quality control within the profession.

After some years of hewing the party line of blind loyalty to the profession, I eventually became convinced that not only our colleagues but also our patients deserved honest and competent support in legitimate grievances. So often the courts had been subjected to the testimony of unscrupulous charlatans and it seemed better for all concerned to have respectable experts stand in their stead, even on the side of the plaintiff. I never sought this role, but having testified successfully on behalf of defendant I was later approached by plaintiff's attorneys, whom I attempted to avoid by agreeing to review the records with the caveat that I would testify on behalf of the client only if I could recognize clear evidence of negligence or malpractice. Lacking that evidence, I would recommend dropping the action and if that recommendation was ignored I would volunteer to testify for the defendant at no charge. To my surprise, the vast majority of who I consider be reputable attorneys were actually pleased to accept that condition, presumably because it was in their interest to avoid pursuing a complaint that would probably not stand up in court. The unscrupulous so-called "experts" would render any opinion that served the lawyer's purpose, insuring a testimony fee regardless of the outcome. My caveat was properly interpreted as a mark of integrity which has served me well in the long run.

The attorneys found occasion to introduce this caveat into the proceedings as a means of establishing my credibility to a jury. On one occasion, however, I happened to testify twice within a month in the same court in Chicago, so the opposition lawyer in the second case learned about the caveat by coming to observe the first case and then successfully petitioned the judge to have it barred from the testimony on the grounds of being self-serving. In that case, the evidence was strongly against his client so his cross examination of my testimony had little effect on his unfavorable position. Instead of dealing with my interpretation of the evidence, he attempted to discredit my veracity by reading numerous seemingly contradictory excerpts from a two foot pile of transcripts of my testimony in previous cases. Not only did he fail to establish any contradictions or statements to his benefit in this boring encounter, but he tripped himself up by reading a passage that just happened to precede a rendition of my dreaded caveat about testifying pro-bono for the opposition. The attorney for whom I was testifying was alert enough to notice this proximity and properly requested that the remainder of that passage be read to the jury, thus circumventing the petition. It was a moment of triumph that resulted in a substantial judgment against a surgeon who had clearly been negligent.

What makes the process interesting is the two phased challenge of conveying a viewpoint effectively. Initially, an opposing attorney takes my deposition to ascertain my position and to probe my deficiencies. The second phase, in front of a jury, consists of dueling with that opposition attorney, who utilizes a large bag of tricks directed at refuting, contradicting and discrediting my testimony. His questions are cleverly framed out of context so as to elicit a self-serving response from which the jury can infer a concession to the opposition. One must be alert so as to respond with an explanation of why the necessarily affirmative answer either belies or is irrelevant to the issue. (Variations of, "Have you stopped beating your wife?"). If a witness provides only passive responses during cross examination his testimony is certain to be weakened. To be effective, the witness under siege must frame his responses to help the jury recognize the attempts at distortion. Sometimes, particularly when the facts in your testimony are essentially irrefutable, the tactic will be to impugn your credibility with questions about how much money you get for testifying, how long it has been since you did this operation, etc. Occasionally an attorney will do an exhaustive search through my testimony in previous cases to expose some inconsistency with my current statements or positions. It has been fortuitous that my posture has always been forthright and consistent, devoid of contrived or distorted answers, because it would be impossible to remember the details and talk my way out of any discrepancies.

It cannot be denied that I fell into this role, in part, as a means of augmenting my marginal income and, in part, to fill a relative void in my formerly frenetic schedule with something that utilized my experience and ability to articulate a position. However, I enjoyed the challenge and the satisfaction of success. My most flattering compliment occurred in a federal court in Brooklyn where my three hour testimony for the defense in a product liability case was followed by a cross examination that was ridiculously brief. At the noon recess, Judge Weinstein dismissed the jury and requested the attorneys to remain for questions from a group of law students who had been observing from the rear of the courtroom. The students' first question was to ask the plaintiff's attorney (who had encountered me in a previous trial) why he had done such a rapid and cursory response to my testimony. His hesitant and sheepish response was, "Every minute that son-of-a-bitch is on the stand I'm losing and I wanted him off as quickly as possible."

Another moment of satisfaction occurred in a Midwestern city where I contended that a near fatal hemorrhage had been the result of egregious negligence. The highly respected defense attorney was a bright, cocky young man whose reputation for courtroom behavior was to be cool, unflappable and in total control. For almost an hour, he attempted to manipulate my testimony to his advantage, but only succeeded in becoming overtly angry, agitated and frustrated. That was as much fun as winning a tennis match. Of course, those times are offset by a few occasions when a clever attorney succeeded in leading me into a trap, but that has been rare.

There is a lot of tedium and some embarrassment in the process of dueling with a manipulative trial attorney. However, it is an invigorating challenge to convince a jury of your viewpoint when a highly-paid, clever opposition attorney is using his skills to obfuscate my testimony or impugn my credibility. It is disillusioning that the outcome of most trials is more dependent on the process than the truth. It would be far more efficient and much more likely to render justice if a panel of experts were selected by the court and queried collectively, without any established relationship to either adversary. Unfortunately, the tort system is too well established for this proposal ever to come about. The economic and social burden of malpractice litigation is reprehensible and I would certainly never be a party to it if my refusal would have any effect on curtailing it. My rationale is that our profession is better served with honest and objective testimony, on either side, than with a fraudulent and distorted opinion, which is easy to solicit.

It is a shame that attorneys get rich on this parasitic process, but the medical profession has only itself to blame for taking so little initiative to establish and enforce standards of care that would disenfranchise those whose performance is substandard. There are many of my colleagues who criticize my participation in a process on behalf of a plaintiff, but my conscience is clear because I have insisted on bringing the truth into the courtroom when harm has been done and because I have succeeded in having many cases dropped before getting to trial.

This unexpected and unintended career as an expert witness became a major occupation that proved to be interesting, challenging and somewhat remunerative. It was fun to utilize my knowledge and academic articulation in a competitive setting.

CHAPTER 24

Mini Crusades

I n keeping with my addiction for tilting at windmills has been my espousal of causes that were usually against conventional thought. Much of that attitude has been related connection with my professional and clinical activities. But other issues, outside medicine, have attracted my unconventional character into becoming an active participant in controversial issues.

The first was my aversion to the "drug war," which I recognized to be both futile and fraudulent. It began many years ago with a visit to the San Francisco coroner to view the autopsy on a patient whose infected and ruptured aortic valve I had replaced with a prosthesis. He had been a heroin addict who had contaminated his blood stream by injecting the drug into his vein with a dirty needle. Unfortunately, the replaced valve also became infected secondarily, in spite of antibiotics. I wanted to see if anything could be learned from the pathology. At that time there were reported to be 18,000 known heroin addicts in the City, so I assumed that the death of my patient was just the tip of a huge iceberg from the consequences of this supposedly "deadly" drug. To my surprise, the coroner denied this assumption and said that the *only* heroin deaths that he saw were caused by the kind of secondary infection my patient had, except for sudden deaths from overdosing, which are not caused by toxicity of the drug but merely by a quantity that the body couldn't handle. Specifically, he verified that he had *never seen or known of any fatal or even serious disease process caused by heroin.* And when I asked him what the addicts died of he responded that most of them just quit the habit spontaneously and died of other natural causes. On further inquiry, he reported that the same facts applied to cocaine and marijuana, neither of which were known, at that time, to have fatal consequences. (It is true that more recently "crack" cocaine can be fatal by eliciting heart rhythm disturbances.)

Since the principal activity of my specialty dealt with the fatal diseases known to be caused by tobacco (lung cancer, coronary heart disease and emphysema), which together account for almost a million deaths a year, I was struck by the irony of outlawing drugs that had never proven to be dangerous if used properly, while allowing—even subsidizing—a substance that is proven to be lethal. Similarly, other legal substances, alcohol and caffeine, are also known to cause serious and fatal diseases. This reality put the enormous cost and massive imprisonment resulting from the drug war into the category of ridiculous. So I wrote an op ed piece on the paradox and the coroner's report—using my professorial title. It was rejected (sequentially) by the *New York Times, Washington Post, Los Angeles Times, Boston Globe, Christian Science Monitor, Chicago Tribune,* and *Philadelphia Inquirer,* presumably because it challenged a firmly established demon. Eventually the *Point Reyes Light,* a Pulitzer Prize winning rural Marin County (CA) Paper did run it and later a slightly different version was published in the *San Francisco Chronicle*[xx]. These endeavors resulted in becoming involved with the Drug Policy Foundation and being asked to speak on the subject. I was invited to join a coalition gathered by Judge Gray that included Meyer Friedman, George Schultz and Joseph McNamara along with prominent law enforcement officials, clergy, and psychiatrists who signed a petition to Congress to change our drug policy.

Altering the established convictions of a misinformed society is very difficult and combating the behemoth of an entrenched bureaucracy is a losing proposition. But I have noted growing recognition that the drug war has not only been a failure, but also that our doubled prison population consists predominantly of non-violent offenders whose only crime was to possess or sell a product for which there is a heavy demand. I have been gratified by the sympathetic response of so many friends and colleagues and a growing dialogue on the subject in the press. Perhaps it is perverse of me to enjoy uphill battles, but I get frustrated at our society being so wantonly and expensively misled.

I have also written about physicians' responsibilities at the end of life. Medical science is responsible for obliterating nearly all of nature's God-given processes that limited the duration of most lives in former generations: cholera, diphtheria, malaria, measles, plague, small pox, syphilis, tuberculosis, typhoid fever, yellow fever, and poliomyelitis to name but a few. And the big killers of this generation heart disease and cancer are being significantly contained to prolong lives. The serious consequence of this miraculous defiance of death is overpopulation and the creation of a huge geriatric population. We are increasingly likely to die a slow lingering death after a massive expenditure of sophisticated technology has struggled to keep us alive, even when the end is imminent. I feel that my profession has an obligation to dispense its wares judiciously and to accept death's inevitability. I wrote an editorial titled "Physician Attitudes About Death"[xxi], in which I promoted a more active role for physicians in the dying process, to act as chaperones and facilitators for the dying—as they are chaperones at birth. Obviously the moral, ethical and legal aspects of this issue are too complex and multiple to be considered here, but I am pleased that so much public attention is being directed to it, hopefully with some benefit. "Right to Die" laws have been passed in some states and people are being encouraged to sign durable power of attorney documents that will allow terminal decisions to be prearranged and carried out.

Heated controversy and careful scrutiny abounds over the physician's legal and moral role in this process. In yesteryear, terminal patients could quietly be given generous doses of narcotics to facilitate their demise without question or recrimination. But unfortunately, the physician's facilitator role has been throttled by legal constraints and whistle blowers. A nursing home whose records reveal more than minimal use of narcotics is in for trouble when the bureaucratic inspectors arrive. Countless lives are being agonizingly and expensively prolonged long after they have ceased to be meaningful to the individual and beyond his/her desires. We are far more humane to our animals than we are to our fellow humans.

Physicians have been trained to focus their full attention and effort on the interests of each individual patient, with little or no consideration of how those interests impact on society at large. Our thriving economy and anti-discrimination laws have essentially mandated "doing everything for everybody," but that behavior is on a collision course with mushrooming and increasingly expensive capabilities that simply cannot be provided to all those who *might* benefit from them. Our profession is aware of this reality but virtually no measures have been addressed to draw the lines and to cease behaving as though everyone *just might* live forever. That will be the most difficult and controversial task that anyone has undertaken. No one seems to have the stomach to grapple with it, but it *has* to be done.

This process of taking a position contrary to conventional thought may seem to be an obsession of mine. But in truth my objectives have never been to disrupt the establishment, with which I basically identify, but rather when I am convinced that the party line is detrimental to society's best interests I am willing to make an issue of it, even at the cost of being identified as a radical.

CHAPTER 25

Dealing With Disability

In my eighty-second year at this writing I can be thankful for robust good health, substantiated by playing tennis three or four times a week and doing the equivalent of two miles on a rowing machine a couple of times each weekend. That achievement, however, obfuscates the problems encountered along the way.

When I was twelve years old, a family physician diagnosed an illness of mine as kidney disease (glomerulonephritis), because some albumin was discovered in my urine and blithely told me that I had—maybe—five years to live. Fortunately, this affliction turned out to be benign Orthostatic Albuminuria and has had no subsequent manifestation, except that it threatened to disqualify me for the Navy until I was able to establish the correct diagnosis.

Almost thirty years ago I was in Chicago for a meeting of the Residency Review Committee, and while exercising in my hotel room by running in place I noted that my left heel intermittently dropped to the floor while my right leg carried the full weight on my toes. I did not notice any disability in running and did nothing about it for a year or more as it progressed only slightly. When I could no longer rise up on my toes, a neurological consultation was finally sought and a diagnosis of Charcot-Marie-Tooth Syndrome was made. Because this is typically an inherited childhood disease that progresses rapidly to a paralyzing death, similar to "Lou Gehrig disease" (ALS), the diagnosis was doubted by most of my medical colleagues. However, nerve conduction studies and a second expert opinion confirmed the diagnosis and predicted a wheelchair in the near future. I am extremely fortunate that progression has been very slow; my weak muscles make climbing difficult, but I am still walking and running—of sorts. I have a brace for my left ankle that prevents my left foot from dropping and improves a modest limp.

In my early 60s I developed severe, disabling pain in my right shoulder from playing tennis. A rotator cuff injury was diagnosed and because shoulder reconstruction was dicey then and I could not take the time from my schedule anyway, it was recommended that I give up tennis. That I was unwilling to do so I started playing left-handed—never having used my left hand for anything except holding and catching—and gradually have restored a semblance of a decent game.

Of interest to my cardiology friends is a sequence of events beginning almost twenty years ago while playing tennis and noticing a slight giddy sensation while resting between sets. I took my pulse and found it to be 190. It caused no distress, did not interrupt the game and disappeared spontaneously. Over the ensuing year or more, I experienced several similar episodes, not always triggered by exercise, all of which disappeared before a diagnosis could be established by EKG. Finally an "attack" occurred while I was eating lunch in the Faculty Club at UCSF and my internist friend Bill Atchley whisked me across the street to the emergency room to have an EKG and capture the aberrant rhythm. It turned out to be an atrial flutter at a regular rate of 380 with a 2:1 "block," which allowed every other impulse to trigger a ventricular beat, thus a pulse of 190. Although this condition is not life-threatening and minimally, if at all, disabling I was put on quinidine and later digoxin which prevented any further episodes of flutter. A year or so later, our baggage was lost on a trip and unavoidably I went without the medication for four days. Nothing happened, so with the option of restarting the medication, I decided not to take it and see if the flutter would reoccur. For ten years there was not a single episode of rhythm disturbance. Then on a recent trip, it reappeared in the middle of the night and responded favorably a few hours later with the reinstitution of digoxin. It is no big deal to continue and I can be grateful for a ten year respite.

Disability can be largely a matter of how one copes with it. I was persuaded to write an article on the subject with particular reference to my amazing classmate, Arthur Guyton, who was struck with bulbar polio while we were surgical residents at the MGH[xxii]. When the experts prognosed a life of total disability Arthur defied them all with amazing determination and persistence to have a productive and outstanding career during which he sired eight children, seven of whom have graduated from Harvard Medical School. His accomplishments would outclass even his most illustrious colleagues even if he had had no disability, but in the presence of what even the most stringent evaluator would classify as *total* disability Arthur is truly a marvel. Determination can forge miracles, and the success of that determination has been greatly enhanced by modern technology. This has convinced me that we should shift our response to disability from pity to encouragement.

CHAPTER 26

My Legacy

Whathat have been the consequences of this long and arguably productive life? What will be remembered and who will remember it? And what would I *like* to have remembered? Have I done anything to make the scene that I leave behind any better than the one into which I arrived?

I think it is fair to say that those who may remember me are likely to think of words like controversial, outspoken and difficult. I would *like* to be remembered for integrity, innovation and perseverance. My technical and clinical contributions will probably be remembered only by those who worked with me and perhaps by those who heard the presentations at a scientific meeting. Improving the quality of performance in my surgical specialty is my greatest pride, but it is doubtful if even those who shared the political endeavor with me will label the achievement with my name. Nevertheless the satisfaction of having accomplished those improvements is great enough that glory is of no import.

The people whose directions and values I may have influenced are the most lasting legacy one can provide. The foregoing narrative is glaringly deficient in description of the family that gave such significant dimension to my life. When I say "family" that naturally includes my wife and children, as well as my parents and a brother and sister. But there is another group whose association was in some ways more intimate, namely the residents and some of the nurses whom I trained and worked with so intensely throughout my career. The surgical and nursing contemporaries with whom I trained at the MGH remain friends who share an important identity. And the members of the board, with whom I spent so many productive hours building mutual respect and sharing a goal of excellence, I must also count as intimates.

I am embarrassed that my selfish engagement in other objectives has caused me to neglect the most important people in my life. It is essential to reiterate my dedication of this manuscript to Jane, in acknowledgment of my love and respect and appreciation of our marvelous partnership as we enjoy each other as much in our twilight years as we did in the fervor of youth. And fortunately, my later years have provided an opportunity for closer rapport with our children. Mutual activity with them has caused me to realize what I had forgotten. Certainly our family life has been happy and sound, albeit stressed by the usual domestic conflicts and, in particular, by the strong-minded characters involved. We all possess a firm conviction that our viewpoints are right, but somehow over the years the conflicts have smoothed out with respect and some concession. I love both of our children very much and I know we are fortunate to have such good relationships with both of them.

Our son David has consistently been an over-achiever whose biography will vastly overshadow this one. His career as an attorney for the Environmental Defense Fund has been successful by introducing and promoting a series of innovative measures to change how industry operates. This high-level tweaking the establishment is paradoxical to his Andover, Yale, Oxford (Rhodes Scholar), and Yale Law School background. He has put his persuasive writing and speaking skills to good use and has an enviable enjoyment in his work. I flatter myself with the thought that some of my maverick behavior has rubbed off on him. His modest life style does not reflect his national success as an innovative and effective environmentalist.

Our daughter Virginia has turned out to be a durable satisfaction, despite being a product of the '60s when rebellion was rampant and parents were so misguided. Her battle with the establishment was compounded by her situation as a mildly dyslectic female sibling who walked in the shadow of a "golden" older brother, leaving her with little room to exceed him. It is not surprising that she took umbrage at the expectations of conventional eldest child parents. She lived with the counterculture and deliberately failed to graduate from U.C. Berkeley by not turning in a senior paper that she had written and which was the only obstacle to her degree. Then she enrolled in a chiropractic college, which, at the time, I regarded as an affront to my career, and she adopted a living relationship with a woman classmate. This was difficult for me to accept for a long time but has evolved happily as we learned to respect and enjoy her partner Delene Bivolcic as a member of the family, and as their professional performance proved to be highly reputable. Happily for all of us Virginia's professional endeavor and her personal relationship both remain successful and sound after twenty years. All of us are on very warm terms.

In addition to my genetic progeny, I have great satisfaction in my professional "children." My residency training program in thoracic surgery at UCSF resulted in close relationships with a series of bright, skilled, mature young surgeons. These men made rounds and operated with me every day. They were stimulating, challenging and rewarding, particularly during that precarious learning period in the new specialty when the traditional teacher/pupil relationship was altered by so much ignorance and uncertainty which we all shared as we learned together. Jointly, we coped with many a harrowing problem as well as enjoying great satisfactions. My progress was their progress because they participated in every innovation and every decision. It is reasonably certain that my impact on their surgical knowledge, their technical skill, their professional performance, and their moral philosophy was greater than on either of my own children.

In all fairness, it should be said that each of those surgical residents, nurses and technicians, who made up our teams that put heart surgery on the map, were supportive and diligent because they shared my satisfactions and frustrations. Noel Fishman was the first graduate of the program to be taken onto the faculty and I remain indebted to him for his loyal help during my political turmoil. Lloyd Rudy was a dynamic and challenging resident who defied my reluctance to do a transplant and made all the arrangements for the one we did. Paul Kelly became the leading cardiac surgeon in Sacramento and was the most faithful follower of my teachings. Bud Smail managed the artificial heart project in the animal laboratory, which was a major undertaking. Joe Utley, who humbly took on the residency after a few years in practice, has been the most successful and productive of my surgical "progeny". Dan Ullyott has been the most successful in terms of his professional recognition as President of both the

American College of Cardiology and the Western Thoracic Surgical Association. Bud Bronstein was resident when Paul Ebert took over my leadership and has been very successful and has remained a loyal supporter over the years. Doris Wellenkamp developed and managed the Intensive Care Unit which played such an important role in postoperative survival. I shall always be indebted for her loyalty and support during the period of invidious gossip. It was she, as head nurse on the Pediatric Floor, who made me aware of how my image was being destroyed. Betty Swenson was a truly remarkable woman who probably could take apart an engine and put it together blindfolded. Her ingenuity and mechanical skill were instrumental in dealing successfully with problems involving extracorporeal circulation; no one will ever know how many lives she saved.

I am very proud of my role in launching the careers of these protégés and equally grateful for their important contributions to my endeavors. Those whose tenure overlapped with Paul Ebert's reign have remained loyal and respectful to offset some of the trauma of my political displacement.

CHAPTER 27

The Bottom Line

The legends and doctrines of religions have never appealed to me because of the horrible tyranny and persecution exercised by their numbers in the process of manipulating human behavior and building expensive and repressive bureaucracies. "God's Will" may be a nice ideal for human behavior and a convenient explanation for what we do not understand, but I am unable to accept the litany of pronouncements and edicts attributed to Him/Her on the basis of tales by historians and theologians, whose sources are questionable, whose interpretations are imaginative, and whose writings have been translated into various meanings.

As for the wishful destiny of an afterlife I have found little to support it. My beliefs are closer to those reflected in the following quotes from the *Rubaiyat* of Omar Khayyam[xxiii].

> I sent my Soul through the Invisible,
>   Some letter of that After-life to spell
> And by and by my Soul return'd to me,
>   And answered: "I Myself am Heav'n and Hell:
> Heav'n but the Vision of fulfill'd Desire,
>   And Hell the Shadow from a Soul on fire,
> Cast on the Darkness into which Ourselves,
>   So late emerged from, shall so soon expire.
>
> And that inverted bowl they call the Sky,
>   Whereunder crawling, coop'd we live and die,
> Lift not your hands to It for help—
>   for It as impotently moves as you or I.

I have no concern about my life's final reckoning, except for the hope that I may have repaid in some part the good fortune that I have enjoyed. It will be for others to decide whether the bottom line is red or black. The foregoing narrative enumerates my indebtedness for so many things: my heritage, both genetic and social, was advantageous; the locale where I grew up and later chose to live is one of the world's most desirable; my education was as good as it gets; my wife is one of the most attractive, interesting and supportive women to be found; my children are bright, healthy, and a great satisfaction; my opportunities have been truly exceptional; the recognition I have received on many fronts has exceeded the performance that led to it; my pleasures and physical comforts have been enviable; my friendships have been many and warm; and my longevity in reasonably good health has exceeded expectation. It all has been enormously satisfying. If I thought there were a deity who had some influence on these events I would thank Him/Her/It profoundly but I am obliged to attribute it all to great luck, which I managed to parlay into a life that was fun, satisfying, and wonderfully unusual.

To what extent I have succeeded in offsetting my obligation to life by contributing something to society, to my profession, and to my family is hard for me to judge. I have made no significant sacrifice for the benefit of others, unless it was to risk my career by taking some stands against convention. My bent for innovation has proven useful, both technically and politically, with some benefit to science and to institutions. I have shared my gains by imparting some knowledge, some skills, some wisdom, and some integrity to my children, to my students, to my residents and to my colleagues. The gratifcation of that is far more valuable to me than any titles or moneys that I have accumulated. Each of those whose lives I have touched will remember me as he/she will. Each of you who has read this personal rendition may give it a different interpretation and a different bottom line.

Amen!

Appendix A

CARDIOTHORACIC RESIDENTS TRAINED BY B.B.R.

John Myers
Abdul AlShamma
John Redington
Donald Elliott
Noel Fishman
Paul Kelly
William Halseth
Lloyd Rudy
Daniel Ullyot
Robert Rawitscher
Joe Utley
W. Carlisle Smail
Vincent Hennessy
Merrill Bronstein

Michael Wood%
Daniel Smith*
David Ellertson*
Kevin Turley*
William Tucker*
James Wilson*
Gus Mavroudis*
Greg Misbach*
Edward Yee*
Edward Verrier*
Robert Tranbaugh*
Scot Merrick%
Frank Hanley%
Jim D'Orsio#

* Residents during Paul Ebert's tenure as dept chairman.
% Residents during Kevin Turley's tenure as interim chief.
# Resident during Donald Magilligan's tenure as chief.

Appendix B

CURRICULUM VITAE OF BENSON B. ROE, M.D.

Education:
University of California, Berkeley: A.B. 1939
Harvard Medical School: M.D.(cum laude) 1943
Massachusetts General Hospital: Surgical Residency 1943–50
Dept. Physiology, Harvard Medical School: National Research Fellow 1948–49
University of Edinburgh: Moseley Travelling Fellow (Harvard) 1950–51

Certification:
American Board Surgery 1950
American Board Thoracic Surgery 1953

Title:
Professor & Chief Emeritus, Cardiothoracic Surgery, U.C.S.F.

Professional Affiliations:
20 National and International Professional Societies, including:
American Surgical Assn., American Assn. for Thoracic Surgery, Society of Thoracic Surgeons, Society of University Surgeons, Society for Vascular Surgery

Current Non-Academic Positions:
Trustee, Avery-Fuller Foundation, Honorary Director Point Reyes Bird Observatory
Editorial Board of *The Pharos*
Editorial Board of *Emedicine*

Former Appointments and Positions:
Chief, Cardiothoracic Surgery, U.C.S.F., 1958–76 (CoChief, 1976–86)
Senior Scientist, Cardiovascular Research Institute, U.C.S.F., 1958–86
Chairman, American Board of Thoracic Surgery, 1981–83 (Director, 1971–83)
President, Society of Thoracic Surgeons, 1973; Chairman, Standards & Ethics Committee

President, Thoracic Surgery Directors Association, 1979–81
President, California Academy of Medicine
Vice President, Society for Vascular Surgery
President, San Francisco Heart Association
Chairman, American College of Surgeons, Advisory Committee for Thoracic Surgery (3 years)
Chairman, American College of Surgeons, Thoracic Surgery Program Committee. (2 years)
Coordinating Committee for Continuing Education in Thoracic Surgery (6 years)
Executive Committee, Council on Cardiovascular Surgery, American Heart Association (4 years)
American Medical Association Residency Review Committee for Thoracic Surgery (6 years)
Editorial Board, Annals of Thoracic Surgery (9 years)
Professional Relations Committee (Fee Review), San Francisco Medical Society
Chairman, Bay Area Research Committee, American Heart Association (2 years)
Board of Directors and Executive Committee, United Bay Area Crusade (5 years)
Liaison Committee of American Association for Thoracic Surgery (6 years)
Cardiovascular Committee, American College of Surgeons (6 years)
Consultant, Joint Harvard–American Medical Association Resource Based Relative Value Fee Study
Councilor-at-Large, Harvard Medical Alumni Council (3 years)
President and Trustee, Miranda Lux Foundation (15 years)
Director, Planned Parenthood, Alameda–SanFranciso
Director, International Bioethics Institute
Director, Point Reyes Bird Observatory
Consultant for Blue Shield of Northern California
Director, Control Laser Corporation

Visiting Professorships:
6 Medical Schools and 3 Clinics in 5 countries
Lectures in 22 countries

Honors:

Silver Medal, American Heart Association;
Rowing Hall of Fame;
Who's Who in America;
Who's Who in the World;
Who's Who in Science and Health Care,
American Men of Science

Bibliography:

175 publications, including 2 Textbooks and 21 Textbook Chapters

References

[i] 1981. "The UCR boondoggle—a death knell for private practice?" *New England Journal Of Medicine* 305: 41-45.

[ii] Roe, B.B. 1980. "A challenge to the health insurance industry." *New England Journal of Medicine* 307: 551-553.

[iii] Coleman, Charles. 1952. *PG&E of California - The Centennial Story.* McGraw-Hill Book Company.

[iv] Ravitch, Mark M., M.D. 1989. "The arrogance of the surgeon." *Surgical Rounds* (February).

[v] Goldthwait, J.C. and B.B. Roe. 1949. "Pulmonary embolism - a statistical study of post mortem material at the Massachusetts General Hospital." *New England Journal of Medicine* 241: 679-686.

[vi] 1951. "Technique for producing pulmonary artery stenosis." *Surgery* 9: 77-81.

[vii] Barger, A.C., G.S. Richardson, and B.B. Roe. 1950. "A method for producing chronic cardiac failure in dogs." *Proc Soc Exper Biol & Med* 73: 113-115.

1950. "Auricular pressure during exercise in dogs with decreased cardiac competence and cardiac failure." *Federation Proc* 9: 7-8.

1952. "Relation of valvular lesions and of exercise to auricular pressure, work tolerance and to development of congestive failure in dogs." *Am. J. Physiology* 169: 384-392.

[viii] Total body perfusion in cardiac operations. Use of perfusate of balanced electrolytes and low molec weight Dextran.

[ix] Bruns, D.L., S.A. Hepps, B.B. Roe, and E. Swenson. 1964. *Arch Surg* 88: 128.

[x] Gardner R.E., S.A. Hepps, and B.B. Roe. 1963. "Amelioration of the pulmonary perfusion syndrome with hemodilution and low molecular weight dextran. *Surgery* 54: 232.

[xi] Tyers, G.F.O. 1975. "The mechanism of myocardial damage following potassium citrate (Melrose) cardioplegia." *Surgery* 78: 45.

[xii] 1977. "Myocardial Protection with cold ischemic cardioplegia." *Thor Cardiovasc Surg* 73: 366.

[xiii] 1962. "Induced ventricular fibrillation to control massive hemorrhage during closed card surgery." *Surgery* 51: 112-120.

[xiv] Kelly, P.B., and B.B. Roe. 1965. "Heat fusion of synthetic suture knots for prosthetic valve implantation. *Ann. Thor. Surg.* 1: 757.

[xv] 1973. "Whither in maturity?" *Annals of Thoracic Surgery* 15: 553-583.

[xvi] Roe, B.B. 1991. "Medical staff privileges: key to safeguarding quality." *Trustee Magazine* (July).

[xvii] Amer. Assn. Thoracic Surg., Soc. Thoracic Surgeons, Amer. Surgical Assn., Amer. College Surgeons & Amer. Medical Assn.

[xviii] Sloan, Herbert, M.D. "The American Board of Thoracic Surgery - A Fifty Year Perspective." *The American Board of Thoracic Surgery.*

[xix] Roe, B.B. 1981. *Perioperative Management in Cardiothoracic Surgery.* Boston: Little, Brown & Co.

[xx] Roe, B.B. "Doctor debunks the war on drugs." *Point Reyes Light* Vol. XLVI No. 26, Sept 17, 1992.

Open Forum, "The Drug War Misses An Important Mark." *San Francisco Chronicle,* November 25, 1992.

[xxi] Editorial, "Physician attitudes about Death." *The Pharos,* Winter 1991.

[xxii] Roe, B.B. "Crippled: who me?" *Harvard Medical Alumni Bulletin,* Spring 1987.

[xxiii] Fitzgerald, Edward (trans.). *The Rubaiyat of Omar Khayyam.* New York: Crosset & Dunlap.

Illustrations